OBJECTS FOR A "WUNDERKAMMER"

The Medici Pax (see page 2)

OBJECTS
FOR A 'WUNDERKAMMER'

Selected and edited by
ALVAR GONZÁLEZ-PALACIOS
Assisted by
LUIGI D'URSO

---

10 June to 31 July 1981

P & D COLNAGHI & CO LTD

14 Old Bond Street, London W1

P & D COLNAGHI & CO LTD

14 OLD BOND STREET, LONDON W1X 4JL
Telephone: 01-491 7408
Telegrams: COLNAGHI LONDON W1
Telex: 298536

OPENING TIMES
Monday–Friday 10 am–6 pm
Saturdays by appointment

PRINTED IN GREAT BRITAIN BY RAITHBY, LAWRENCE & COMPANY LTD, LEICESTER AND LONDON

CONTENTS

ACKNOWLEDGEMENTS

P. & D. Colnaghi joins with the Editor in thanking the following people for their help and advice in the preparation of this catalogue:

Count Franco Arese, Daniela Di Castro, Andrew Ciechanowiecki, Tim Clarke, George Daniels, Professor Antonio Giuliano, John Hayward, John Harris, Professor Detlef Heikamp, Cyril Humphris, Alastair Laing, Tina Miller and Alessandro Orsi. Thanks are also due to John Winter for a loan, to other lenders who wish to remain anonymous, and most especially to M. Jacques Petit-Horry for the generous loan of his two important bronzes from the French Royal Collection. We would also like to express our warmest thanks to those who helped with the actual production of the catalogue: Prue Cuming and her assistants for photographs; Maggie Boardman, Jill Elvin and Jean Fraser for typing and re-typing the entries; Philip Jebb for designing the show-cases; Ursula Lanz for arranging the publicity; Michael Unwin of Raithby Lawrence for patience beyond the call of duty, and above all Katherina Mayer-Haunton and Adrian Eeles whose editorial contributions to the catalogue have been of the greatest possible benefit.

Finally, we are very grateful to the various experts who have provided the catalogue entries, all of which are signed with their initials:

C. A.	Charles Avery
R. J. C.	Robert J. Charleston
J. A. C.	Juliusz A. Chrościcki
R. F.	Richard Falkiner
M. G.	Michael Goedhuis
A. G.-P.	Alvar González-Palacios
J. H.	John Hayward
D. K.	Donald King
M. M.	Margaret Medley
E. J. P.	Edward J. Pyke
D. S.	Diana Scarisbrick
R. S.	Robert Skelton
L. d'U.	Luigi d'Urso
C. W.	Clovis Whitfield

INTRODUCTION

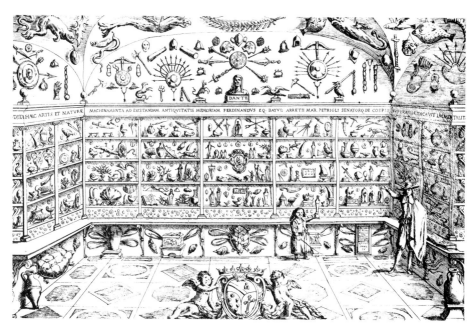

The *Museo Cospiano,* from an engraved frontispiece for *Il Museo Cospiano annesso a quello del famoso Ulisse Aldrovandi,* Bologna, 1677.

"FROM WUNDERKAMMER TO MUSEUM"

On 3rd May, 1787 Goethe, travelling through Sicily, visited the Palace of the Prince of Biscari in Catania, and saw the collections formed by the Prince's father, Ignazio Paternó Castello (1719–1786) who had died the year before[1]. He was interested by what he saw and, as usual, gave a very careful account of it:

"Early this morning, the Abbé, who had already come to pay his respects yesterday, arrived and took us to the palace. We first visited the museum with its collection of marble and bronze statues, vases and many other such antiquities. We were fascinated by a torso of Jupiter, which I already knew from a cast in Tischbein's studio, but which has greater merits than one would guess from the cast. A member of the household gave us the most essential historical information. Next we were taken to the Prince, who showed us his collection of coins. This was a special mark of confidence since, both in his father's day and in his own, several objects were missing after they had been shown to visitors, and he was now chary of showing them. I had learned a good deal from looking at Prince Torremuzza's collection, and added to my knowledge by reading Winckelmann, whose book provides a reliable thread to guide us through the various epochs of art, so this time I was able to do much better. When he saw that, though amateurs not connoisseurs, we were observant, the Prince, who is an expert in these matters, willingly explained to us everything we wanted to know. After spending some time, though not enough, over these objects, we were about to take our leave when he took us to his mother's suite to see the rest of his smaller works of art.

"There we were introduced to a distinguished-looking lady; with an air of instinctive breeding she opened the glass cabinet in which the amber collection was kept. What distinguishes Sicilian amber from the northern kind is that it passes from the colour of transparent or opaque wax or honey through all possible shades of yellow to a most beautiful hyacinthine red. We were shown urns, cups and other things which had been carved from it, and it was clear that remarkably large pieces must have been needed. These, some incised shells from Trapani and some exquisite ivories were the lady's special pride and joy, and she had some amusing stories to tell about them."

As a final comment he adds: "The Prince, on the other hand, spoke about more serious matters and in this manner we spent some entertaining and instructive hours."

We can therefore assume that amber, ivories and shells were not considered very serious objects, even by a man of insatiable curiosity such as Goethe, yet the great German writer was not uninterested in precious objects. Whilst translating Cellini's autobiography, for instance, he rediscovered the gold salt, that is now the pride of the Kunsthistorisches Museum in Vienna but was then forgotten. In the passage quoted Goethe mentions the name of a man who was responsible to a considerable degree for the change of taste which had taken place over the previous thirty years, that of his compatriot Winckelmann – initiator of a new approach to art that can be summed up by the memorable phrase "noble simplicity and quiet grandeur". Those were the principles of Classic Art: this exhibition presents the obverse, like a double-headed Janus.

The focus of attention here is amber, ivories and shells, rather than simplicity and grandeur as conceived by Winckelmann. And yet the story of Art has (like the serpent biting its tail that symbolises eternity) no beginning and no end; if it is true that the *Wunderkammern* contributed little to the understanding of classic art, they did not necessarily exclude its products. It is generally agreed that Winckelmann acquired his enthusiasm for Antiquity in Dresden through studying some of the statues bought by Augustus the Strong. The sovereign was at one and the same time one of the last owners of an important *Wunderkammer* and one of the first creators of a modern museum. In 1720 he unscrambled the extraordinary jumble of all sorts of objects accumulated by his ancestors since the second half of the XVIth century and divided them into a Gallery of Paintings, a Print Cabinet, a Porcelain Collection (in the Japanisches Palais), an Armoury, and the famous Grünes Gewölbe, where precious things were exhibited to the public. He also bought antiquities from Rome and formed what was then regarded as the most important collection of classical sculpture in northern Europe. Other objects, like clocks and scientific instruments, were sent to a special cabinet in the Zwinger, and an anatomical museum, a zoological museum and a mineralogical collection were all set up on their own[2]. In spite of the ravages of terrible wars the wealth and the quality of these collections is still unsurpassed. It must be remembered, however, that their origins lay in a mind that combined the omnivorous appetite of a Baroque Prince with the curiosity of a Renaissance intellect and the discernment of a *philosophe* of the Age of Reason. Is the same not true of the Medici collections which are still today the glory of Florence? They are the product of the enthusiasms of several generations; yet their beginnings were the same as those of Saxony, a private collection intended to lend prestige to a ruling house, and has since become a museum, or rather, a series of museums.

It may be time to pose the question, what is a *Wunderkammer*? Julius von Schlosser, the celebrated Viennese art historian, wrote an entire book about the subject in 1908[3], so it will be understood that the answer to this question cannot be formulated in a few lines. As an over-simplification one might say that it is a collection of remarkable objects: and that this includes things not only made by the genius of man but also by the caprice of nature-*artificialia, naturalia* and *curiosa* – everything being placed on the same level and with no consideration of chronology or common provenance. The rarer a thing was, the more attractive it appeared, be it a bone of a giant or a jewel by a famous goldsmith. So it was that in the same room in the Palazzo Vecchio in Florence, Cosimo I (according to an inventory of his possessions drawn up in 1553) had *un cuccudrillo grande* and *una testa di S.E. do bronzo tocca d'oro di mano do Benvenuto Cellini*[4]. What did a stuffed or mummified crocodile have to do with one of the greatest portraits of the Renaissance? What was the magical rapport between a human effigy and an animal which was still regarded as rather mysterious? Did a crocodile symbolise medicine, or was it perhaps regarded as an amulet against illness by XVIth century man, still imbued with beliefs that were not very remote from those of the Middle Ages? Was the crocodile a deity like Sebekh in ancient Egypt, to whom a temple was dedicated in Kom Ombo: a god to be placated in order to avoid any harm from his vindictive nature? For the Renaissance, magic, astrology, and the esoteric sciences, were all aspects of a single phenomenon, along with the exactitude of chronometry and the idealisation of reality in painting or sculpture: monstrosities and platonic ideas of form and beauty were the *recto* and the *verso* of the same medal.

All this encyclopaedic knowledge was concentrated in the sombre rooms that held these collections. The sunlit calm of the Greek and Roman Gods co-existed with the necromantic obscurity of strange roots and stones: alchemy and magic were intertwined with philosophy. Lorenzo the Magnificent, for example, received a letter from the poet Poliziano dated 20th June 1491, which announced the arrival of a fine ancient Greek vase presented by a Venetian nobleman. *Il Magnifico* also had in his rooms the famous *Battle Scenes* by Paolo Uccello, and owned, among many other things, the masterpieces of neo-Alexandrine refinement by Botticelli which we admire in the Uffizi; yet the horn of a unicorn, which was probably the same one that had belonged to his father Piero de'Medici (*un chorno di unicorno leghato in oro*) was valued at a much higher price than the Greek amphora or any of his paintings[5].

Charles V, a man of more troubled mentality, took few things with him to his retreat in Yuste after he abdicated from the Empire and the Kingdoms of this world: yet these included both a famous altar-piece by Titian, and a considerable number of clocks and watches. He did more; he forced the famous Italian clockmaker Gianello Torriano to join him in order to construct an astronomical clock that required three years of work to complete. His passion for this type of instrument was such that his cook once made him laugh–something which did not happen often – when he suggested an omelette of watches to appease his insatiable hunger – a truly Arcimboldesque concept.

Charles, the champion of Catholicism, also had with him in his final days the crucifix that his wife had kissed during her last minutes on earth and a number of gold amulets containing various stones (one against the flux of blood, another against leprosy, a third against gout) and a variety of English rings supposed to be effective against the pains of cramp[6].

It is probably impossible to establish when men started to collect extraordinary or mysterious objects. Schlosser pointed out that in Europe the origins of such collections were to be found in the treasuries of mediaeval churches, in which relics, mementos and trophies were preserved. Yet beautiful monstrosities were also admired in Antiquity: to mention only one example, Suetonius recalls that: "Augustus had his houses embellished, not only with statues and pictures but also with objects which were curious by reason of their age and rarity, like the huge remains of monstrous beasts which had been discovered on the Island of Capri, called giants' bones or heroes' weapons"[7]. Things monstrous or bizarre have invariably attracted men, especially in that period when religious dogma or philosophical beliefs were not strong enough to control morbid imaginations. Rarity and exoticism go hand in hand; in every *Wunderkammer* one finds elements of *Orientalia, Africana, Americana* and *Antiquaria*. A collector born before the revolution in taste brought about by Winckelmann could easily exhibit a Mogul miniature next to the bust of a Roman Emperor, a rhinoceros horn, a piece of amber, a maiolica vessel (of the kind often thought to be early works by Raphael), an astrolabe, a medal of a *condottiere*, a wax effigy of a beloved or famous person, and great works of art by living artists. It could be said that such a collection was *un teatro delle cose naturali*, as the Bolognese scientist and collector Ulisse Aldrovandi wrote in the late XVIth century, anticipating a Baroque concept.

All the types of object enumerated above appear for instance in the Museum of Cardinal Flavio Chigi I (1641–1693), who displayed them together with the drawings by Bernini that are today in the Vatican[8]. Although the difference between a masterpiece by a famous artist and works of applied art (as they have been called in English since the XIXth century) had begun to be recognised this did not interfere with the attitude of rulers, collectors and artists themselves. To Louis XIV it was all the same whether Lebrun was painting the vault of the Galerie des Glaces or designing furniture. Distinctions came later and culminated in the last century.

Some collectors had gone quite far with their peculiar enthusiasms; the Landgrave of Hesse-Cassel, who owned one of the most precious *Kunst-und Wunderkammern*, in Germany had a cat-harpsichord, that is to say a musical instrument whose sound was obtained by pulling the tails of cats boxed up in a wooden case. Philip II admired one of these sadistic instruments in Brussels in 1545. Some of the great painters of the XVIth century bowed to this sort of taste for the abnormal, for instance, Bronzino, who portrayed the dwarf Morgante seen from the front and from behind. In the XVIIth century an artist as great as Velázquez reveals a fascination with jesters, dwarfs, cripples, hunchbacks and *bobos* (idiots); not to speak of the malicious caricatures by Carreño such as the poor girl of disproportionate girth and tiny height whom he painted both naked and dressed (as Goya was later to paint his Maja in an erotic vein).

Living dwarfs had their own *raison d'être* in this world of monsters; every great lord of the Renaissance had at least one. The ducal palace at Mantua still contains living quarters expressly built for these miniature people, who may be said to have inspired Victor Hugo's *Le Roi s'amuse* and Verdi's *Rigoletto*. During the Enlightenment it was still a matter of prestige to own a dwarf. The words of the Abbé Lalande, one of the most observant travellers of the XVIIIth century, tell us about this particular fashion in the precious prose of his Neapolitan diary of 1765: "*La Princesse* (de Francavilla) *a chez elle un nain qui appartenait il y a quelques années au Cardinal Valenti, dont la hauteur n'est que 3 pieds 3 pouces, quoiqu'il ait 27 ans; il n'est pas aussi singulier, ni d'une forme aussi naturelle & aussi svelte que le Comte Borowlaskii Polonais, que nous avons vu à Paris en 1759, & qui n'avoit que 28 pouces, ou le Nain du Ro, Stanislas, appelé Bebet, qui avoit trois pieds; quant aux facultés de l'ame, il tient à peu-près au milieu entre ces deux, dont le premier avoit beaucoup d'esprit & de talent & le second etoit presque imbécille"*[9]. A dwarf therefore was in a certain sense part of the *Wunderkammer*. We are unable to say whether they were always clever or stupid; the one who appears on the frontispiece of the book about one of the most famous of these collections, the *Museo Cospiano* (published in Bologna in 1677) has the air of a professor; he was certainly more intelligent than Bebet.

Naturally, giants were of equal interest. While visiting Schloss Ambras, which houses the collections of Archduke Ferdinand of Tyrol (one of the greatest connoisseurs of the XVIth century), J. G. Keysler remarked: "Against the wall stands the wooden-image of one Aymon, who belonged to the archduke Ferdinand's bodyguards; he was eleven feet in height, but did not live much beyond his fortieth year. The famous Baron Bentenrieder the Imperial minister, who also did not reach any great age, was eight feet eight inches high; travelling this way, some years ago, he measured himself with this wooden giant, but hardly reached up to Aymon's armpits"[10].

Still-life painters were equally attracted by natural monstrosities, especially in the Baroque period. For example the Tuscan Bartolomeo Bimbi portrayed at various times many gigantic or abnormal fruits in order to please the ambivalent tastes of his lord, Grand Duke Cosimo III. The work of the XVIIth century Lombard Giuseppe Arcimboldo, who worked for the Emperor Rudolph II in Prague, was in a different vein. One of the most morbid spirits of the late Mannerist period, collector of infinite passion, Rudolph II, with his ambiguous eroticism, his necrophiliac instincts and his endless curiosity, is the perfect incarnation of the type of Prince that interests us here. Art seeking to imitate the working of nature reached a pitch of the utmost refinement in the XVIth century and tried to surpass nature herself, mixing every element in every fantastic combination possible. Such artifice and sophistication formed the basis of the *Wunderkammer*: it found its highest expression in the paintings of Arcimboldo, the inventor of extraordinary and anthropomorphic still-lives, allegories of the greatest extravagence that probably hid moral implications behind the pure pleasure in the *agudeza* of the invention. In *Fire*, one of his most famous pictures, the flames and the various utensils connected with this element are formed into a human, or to be more accurate, vaguely human effigy. The entire Mannerist culture expressed itself in an ambiguous language searching for effects which were marvellous and, as already been said, monstrous. This is even reflected in the work of the goldsmiths employed by Rudolph, such as Paulus van Vianen.

The search for ever even more complex mechanisms obsessed the artisans of the XVIth century, who constructed numerous automata and sophisticated pieces of apparatus that, although without practical use, were ideal for the *Wunderkammer*. The very beautiful locks that no key could open, the trap-armchairs that imprisoned those incautious enough to sit on them, and curious and useless instruments of torture, were all intended for this sort of collection. Very elaborate watches and machines able to emit the sounds of various instruments were fitting company for them. The presence of such instruments at Ambras, where some of them are still exhibited, confirms the passionate interest aroused by such prodigies of technology pushed to the limits of virtuosity. This was an enthusiasm which did not simply stop at the object but even led the collector to keep the tools used in the work and often to take part in the construction of the works of art themselves. Grand Duke Francesco I of Florence, like his brother-in-law Ferdinand of Tyrol himself made part of the objects that he collected and followed the progress of research day by day. This sometimes produced extraordinary results, such as when a method of making porcelain was discovered for the first time in Europe. The Medici had always been avid collectors of oriental porcelain, at least as far back as the time of Il Magnifico's father, Piero. Francesco I's brother, Ferdinand (while still a cardinal in Rome), sent a present of Chinese porcelain to Christian of Saxony, some of which has recently been identified in Dresden. On the other hand, Francesco I sent Philip II of Spain some of his own Medici porcelain (two flasks from this group are now in the museum at Sèvres). Ferdinand of Tyrol was a dilettante architect and founded a manufactory with a lathe, a chemical laboratory, and a foundry, as well as a glass-house, where he himself, seated next to the artisans, blew and formed glass into eccentric forms, some of which are still in Vienna and at Ambras.

Glass with its infinite malleability, rock-crystal and *pietra-dura* vases, sometimes with strange shapes and virtuoso pieces of Murano glass, filled various cupboards at Ambras, and still form an almost unique ensemble (although some of the best pieces have been transferred to Vienna).

Rare materials with their mysterious and magic virtues continued to attract collectors in the XVIth century. Coral branches entered their cabinets happily combined with shells, or with ostrich eggs mounted in gold and silver. As has been said, these ensembles, which were usually made in Southern Germany, demonstrate the pleasure with which the creations of nature were regarded, especially after their artistic transformation and elaboration in the manner inherited from the Middle Ages. Of course these ostrich eggs do not have the same meaning attributed to the supposed one that can be seen hanging above the Virgin's head in Piero della Francesca's picture in the Brera (whose abstruse religious significance is discussed in an essay by Millard Meiss).

Where were all these fantastic objects made? Sometimes, as has already been suggested, princes created their own manufactories and engaged craftsmen and artists who worked only for them. The first to do so were the Medici, who patronised workshops as complicated as they were efficient, which in the beginning, under Cosimo I, were headed by Vasari; later the Grand-Duke Francesco summoned many artisans to Florence from other cities, and afterwards his brother Ferdinand reorganised the workshops and gave them a proper administrator in the person of the Roman nobleman Emilio de' Cavalieri. The *Stanzino* (now commonly called the *Studiolo*) which Francesco made for himself in the Palazzo Vecchio, is the perfect counterpart of a German *Wunderkammer*; there is a clearer sense of order in it, however, which is different in feeling from the "witches kitchens" (as Schlosser defined the more sinister collections on the other side of the Alps). The Florentine *Studiolo* was designed by Vasari with scrupulous and exquisite perfection. All the allegories that adorn it are a compendium of the Latin love of every form of artistic expression. The *Galleria dei lavori*, that is to say the Grand-ducal workshops, were afterwards housed on the second floor of the Uffizi, where every sort of activity continued until well into the XVIIIth century. The example of Florence was followed in Prague by Rudolph II, and later on in Paris, under Louis XIV and Colbert, at the Gobelins. The King of

Naples, Don Carlos, called many Florentine artisans to his capital after the death of the last Medici Grand Duke, Gian Gastone, in 1737, and founded a series of Royal workshops; later, when he became King of Spain as Charles III, he started the manufactories of the Buen Retiro in Madrid. But of course objects were also bought from individual craftsmen working in cities like Milan, Augsburg and Nuremberg, which became famous for their productions in this field. Special agents were sent to the East or to European ports like Lisbon and Antwerp to procure the rare and beautiful artifacts of the Orient.

As has already been said, by the XVIIIth century the enthusiasm for things strange and rare began to be ousted by the proper study and classification of antiquity and natural objects; whilst instead of trying in vain to make gold through alchemy, the secret of porcelain was rediscovered. This was a material that had first been imported into Europe by Marco Polo at the end of the XIIIth century and that had been collected ever since by every powerful lord. As has been seen, the first city to produce porcelain was Florence. The experiment did not last long and it was in Saxony, in the small town of Meissen near Dresden, that Augustus the Strong founded the first European manufactory, which is still active today.

The owners of *Wunderkammern*, ignorant of the celestial discoveries of Galileo, lived in a world in which the earth remained fixed in heavens of impenetrable darkness with stars that shone brightly with a light as yet unexplained. Though this is partly true for the Renaissance and Early Baroque, in the age of Enlightenment the collector's approach to science, which had consisted mainly of a study of virtuosity and rarity, started to develop. The minds of men were no longer obsessed by the perfection of a piece of mechanism or the exquisite carving of a stone. *Objets de vertu*, as they are uniquely known in England, began to be outmoded. Antiquity was regarded from an artistic, a political and philosophical point of view. To become a sage perhaps implies to become cynical or, more precisely, to try to observe things as they are. Poetic licence was slowly abandoned as the earth started to move in the heavens. The *virtuosity* of an object still attracted many – and rightly still does so today – but its meaning or, as we would say now, its message, became of paramount significance. Curious or *virtuous* objects began to be relegated to scientific collections – to the first natural history museums. Art was required not only to appeal to a love of the curious, but it had to teach a moral lesson, to convey the great example of the ancient world's ethics and civic spirit.

In the XVIIIth and XIXth centuries great technical improvements were made, but it was felt that these should be used more for public enlightenment than for the pleasure of the sovereign alone, thus establishing the principles of the modern museum. The more civilised or prosperous a country became, the more destruction was perpetrated in the Paradise Lost of the *Wunderkammer*; this is why the better-preserved ones are located in secondary courts or castles, such as Ambras or Rosenborg. Some of the most elaborate pieces of furniture of Louis XIV, for instance, were destroyed, and if some fragments were saved by Buffon, it was because he obtained them from the Royal Gardemeuble for the museum of Natural History (which is today the Jardin des Plantes) as examples of minerals, and not as works of art in their own right. What we consider a work of art today, was not necessarily regarded with the same respect in the XVIth or XVIIth centuries, nor even in the XVIIIth. Caravaggio's famous *Medusa* was exhibited in the Uffizi Armoury along with a Persian suit of armour, as Richard Lassels, who was there in 1670 recalls: "Then I saw the Armour for Horse and man of two kings of Persia . . . the buckler with the Medusa head on it, painted by Michael Angelo. A Turkish Bell to ring in time of Battel . . ."[11]. It is curious to reflect on the destiny of this strange picture, which was considered a work of Michaelangelo by Lassels, whilst in the XIXth century Walter Pater analysed it as a masterpiece by Leonardo.

Well into the XVIIth century, the taste for *Wunderkammer* had still not disappeared, even if it was mingled with the new era's love of novel materials. The wax exhibited here by N. E. Cetto belongs to this chapter of the history of taste, as does the *piqué* mirror frame sent by the King of Naples to his mother (catalogue numbers 79 and 121) just as the love of *chinoiserie* (a new form of home-made exoticism) did not stop the Age of Reason from appreciating the sublime forms of Antiquity. In the same fashion, cities that had specialised in this sort of commerce, continued to flourish as Keysler noted during his visit to Augsburg in about 1740: "An incredible quantity of Turkish, as it is called, and other sorts of gold and silver paper is made here, and at so cheap a rate, that the workmen can scarce earn half a guilder a day. Mr. Mann, a silversmith, has cabinets, looking-glasses, and scrutores of excellent workmanship, finely painted and decorated with amber, mother-of-pearl, lapis lazuli, and agate, and columns of amethyst. The master himself is now in Vienna, disposing of a looking-glass, a table, and two stands for candlesticks of this kind of work for twenty thousand dollars, *Seuter* sells the finest porcellane, most of which he has plain and white from Dresden but afterwards he adds greatly to their value by nice paintings and enamels. He also has by him above a hundred earthen dishes painted by Francisco Duranei, who lived about the middle of the fifteenth century, and though not comparable to Raphael of Arbin's are not without their beauty. this work must immediately be varnished, and but once into the fire; which as yet is the ne plus ultra of that art."

However, the XVIIIth century was not an era for *Wunderkammern*. They were resuscitated in a different form during the Romantic period in reaction against what had been done under Napoleon, when Vivant-Denon created in Paris the largest museum that has ever existed. The great collectors of the XIXth century re-acquired a taste for rarities that was epitomised in what is called the *goût-Rothschild*, a mélange of the precious and remarkable in a setting of comfort and luxury, which was transferred to America by people like J. Pierpont Morgan and H. C. Frick. Before that the stylistic revivals that were known in German as *Historismus*, had already produced imitations or straightforward fakes; we exhibit a couple of these objects here although this could be the subject of another chapter.

What the true *Wunderkammer* comprised is exemplified by the museum formed by the Jesuit Anthanasius Kircher (1602–1680), a man of polymathic interests, who wrote about telescopes, fossils, shells, music, physics, Egyptian antiquities and hieroglyphics, optics and colour. He was a German scholar living in Rome whose museum was located in the Jesuit Collegio Romano (the remains of which are today in the Museo Pigorini). Keysler, whom we have already quoted twice, visited it during his travels. It may prove useful to the reader to glance at a list of the incredible variety of things that the erudite priest owned, since it embodies the guiding principles of Beauty and Knowledge that this exhibition too tries to reflect.

Alvar González-Palacios

The *Museum Kircherianum*, which is divided in several closets, might have been much better arranged than it is; however, it contains a multitude of curiosities, among which I shall set down the following:

1. Utensils, as spoons, knives, writing instruments, etc., of foreign and distant nations, particularly the *Chinese*.
2. Exotic birds and skeletons; and among these is one with three legs.
3. Monstrous eggs, adders, and other natural productions.
4. Insects, tarantulas, etc., double-tailed lizards, etc.
5. Flour and bread made of a *Brazil* root called *Beiu*, both very white.
6. Salts of all kinds; among which, that dug near *Cordona* is remarkably white and hard.
7. A lizard enclosed in a piece of amber.
8. *Flos ferri*, of a fine white colour, taken from the *Styermark* mines.
9. Rare and uncommon fishes; among others, the *Orbis*, a fish so called from its orbicular figure, being as round as a ball.
10. *Calculi*, of stones taken out of human bodies; particularly one weighing 10 ounces, found in the bladder of *P. Leo Sanctius*.
11. Ivory works curiously turned.
12. Some attempts towards perpetual movement.
13. Several ancient pictures of womens' heads, with their hair finely ornamented; under these is the following inscription from *Tertullian de cultu foeminarum*:

    Crinibus harum quiescere non licet.

    "They never suffer their hair to rest".

    To which may be added the following from *Terence*:

    Nostin' mores mulierum,

    Dum moliuntur, dum comuntur, annus eft*

    "You know the custom of the ladies, who take a vast deal of time in dressing themselves, and combing their hair".
14. Several kinds of *Indian* fruits.
15. Optic drawings.
16. Chinese work.
17. Clockwork, and musical *automata*.
18. Corals, and several other vegetables from the *Mediterranean*, the *Red Sea*, and the ocean.
19. Mechanical inventions and machines for lifting weights.
20. A fine collection of several kinds of marble, agate, alabaster, together with their names, and this inscription:

    In scopulis quoque ipsis and lapidibus reperit natura in quo delectaret. S. Ambros. Proefat. in Psalmos.

    "The very rocks and stones have afforded entertainment to those who study nature".
21. The bezel of a ring found in an ancient Christian tomb, having engraved on it a dolphin and an anchor, with these *Greek* characters: IXOTC; i e., a *Fish*; some interpret this in a mystical sense.
22. Earthen utensils of all countries, porcelain of *Japan, China, Persia,* etc.
23. Busts of the ancient emperors, likewise a statue of the *Virgin Mary*, with the infant *Jesus*, consisting of little pearls of different colours, *Masgaritini*, etc.
24. Pieces of writing in miniature; among which is *Solomon's Song* in *Hebrew*, included in a very narrow compass. Some of these works of penmanship represent portraits, etc.
25. Curious shells.
26. Earthen vases, said to be painted by *Raphael*.
27. Pictures of celebrated persons, as *Petrarch, Michael Angelo*, etc.
28. Hats, caps, etc., made of the fibres of exotic trees and leaves.
29. Petrefactions, *Malta* vipers' tongues, elephants' teeth, fossil ivory, etc. Among the petrefactions, the most remarkable is a whole human body turned to stone.
30. *Tabulae votivae*, or votive pieces, amulets, etc.

31. Ancient inscriptions, among which is one *Volcano Quieto Augusto*.
32. Antique *stili*, or writing instruments, bracelets, bells and keys.
33. Antique seals, weights, etc.
34. Instruments used in ancient sacrifices.
35. Points of the darts of spears used by the ancients.
36. Antique bronzes; ancient monuments on the settlement of a colony, being a plough drawn by two calves, two oxen, and a man.
37. Bows, arrows, shields, and other arms of savage nations.
38. A great number of marble *basso-relievo's*, and idols of several nations.
39. Small earthen vessels from several foreign countries, of delicate workmanship.
40. Earthen antique lamps.
41. Urns, a great many of which are very deep; vasa lacrymatoria, etc.
42. Heads of ancient statues, antique masks of several kinds, etc.
43. Bones of large animals.
44. The natural weapons of several animals, as the horn of a *Rhinoceros*, a *Unicorn's* horn, etc.
45. *Egyptian* mummies.
46. A large collection of sea shells; among which, one called the Priest's Cap, is of such a venomous nature, that the least wound of it is mortal.
47. A large tile inscribed thus: + *Rege Dom. nostro Theodorico felix Roma*.
48. Inscriptions on marble; a fragment of the *Fasti Consulares*; a very scarce medal, representing the adoration of the easter *Magi*, of the size of a *dollar*, but thinner.
49. *Hetruscan* antiquities.
50. Salts and crystals.
51. Glass and enamelled works, most of them antiques.

BIBLIOGRAPHY

1. On the Prince's personality and collections see the recent essay by L. Storoni Mazzolani, *Il ragionamento del Principe di Biscari,* Palermo, 1980 (with all previous bibliography). It should be noticed that the Ignazio Paternó Castello had collected both the curiosities and the antiquities in the palace.
2. See the essay by J. Menzhausen in the exhibition catalogue *The Splendor of Dresden,* New York, 1978.
3. J. von Schlosser, *Die Kunst – und Wunderkammern der Spätrenaissance,* Leipzig, 1908.
4. C. Conti, *La prima reggia di Cosimo I de' Medici,* Florence, 1893, p. 80.
5. E. Müntz, *Les collections des Medicis au XVe Siècle,* Paris, 1888. The author already noted (p. 54) that the unicorn was now priced at 6,000 florins while pictures by the most famous masters were not valued at more than 100 florins each. However, *"Una Schodella di Sardonio et Calcidonio et agatha, entorj piu figure et di fuori una testa di Medusa",* that is to say the *tazza Farnese* (today in the Museo Nationale, Naples) was valued at 10,000 florins.
6. W. H. Prescott, *Gli ultimi anni di Carlo V,* Palermo, 1978. Cosimo I also owned *"Una fascia di tela legatoi sette pietre in argento che hanno virtu".* Conti, *op. cit.,* p. 155.
7. Suetonius, *Life of the Caesars: Augustus,* chapter 72.
8. G. Incisa delle Rocchetta, "Il museo di curiosità del card. Flavio I Chigi", *Archivio della Società Romana di Storia patria,* 1967, Vol. XX, fasc. I-IV, pp. 141–192.
9. [Lalande], *Voyage d'un françois en Italie,* Venice, 1769, Vol. VI, p. 142.
10. J. G. Keysler, *Travels through Germany, Bohemia, Hungary, Switzerland, Italy and Lorraine,* London, 1756, Vol. I, p. 31. Keysler's famous book was first published in Germany in 1740–1741.
11. R. Lassels, *The Voyage of Italy,* Paris, 1670, p. 166; D. Heikamp, "La Medusa del Caravaggio e l'armatura dello Scià Abbàs di Persia", *Paragone,* September 1966, no. 199, pp. 62–76.
12. Keysler, *op. cit.,* p. 75.

FURTHER BIBLIOGRAPHY

It would be impossible to give here a complete list of books and articles dealing with the subject of this Exhibition. It may however prove useful to name at least the following writings which contain further bibliographical data. Many other books are listed in the individual entries.

The various catalogues of the exhibition *Firenze e la Toscana dei Medici nell'Europa del Cinquecento* (Florence, 1980) and that of the exhibition *Livorno e Pisa: due città e un territorio nella politica dei Medici* (Pisa, 1980). Of use will be the catalogue *Barock in Deutschland Residenzen* (Berlin, 1966) and most specially E. Scheicher's *Die Kunst-und Wunderkammern der Habsburger* (Vienna-Munich-Zurich, 1979). Not to be forgotten are D. Heikamp's pioneering studies, mainly "Zur Geschichte der Uffizien-Tribuna und der Kunstschrnke in Florenzä und Deutschland", *Zeitschrift für Kunstgeschichte*, 1963, pp. 193–268; and *Mexico and the Medici*, Florence, 1972. A book by various authors *Le Arti del Principato Mediceo,* Florence, 1980. See also exhibition catalogue *Stilleben in Europa,* Münster-Baden Baden, 1980.

METALWORK

PAX OF THE MEDICI.
Rome, early XVIth century.

On the front of this *africano* marble and silver gilt pax, the Sybil shows to
the kneeling Augustus the apparition of the Virgin and Child. Their images
are formed by the veining of the marble itself, framed by a halo of rays of
silver gilt appliqué. Over the Virgin an appliqué cartouche with the inscription: *HEC EST ARACELI.* Frame with palmettes alternating with
rosettes in circles at the corners; two handles at the sides. From the top
corners little chains join in a pendant with the Medici arms surmounted by
ribbons and enclosed by ivy leaves.

On the back the frame is only outlined and marked at the corners by
palmettes; in the middle a convex rectangular cartouche with the inscription:

> *NON.HOC. TERRA.DEDIT.GEMMA.PRETIO —*
> *SIUS.OMNI.*
> *AETHEREA.SUMMUS.MISIT. AB.ARCE.DEUS.*

> *QUAM.VATES.QUAM.FATA.CANUNT.SA —*
> *CRAEQUE.SYBILLAE.*
> *VIRGINIS.EXIGUO.MARMORE. IMAGO*
> *PATET.*

Dimensions: H. 14 cm; L. 11.5 cm

The pax was, and is, offered to the faithful for a ritual kiss before communion.
Usually they have only one handle on the back; in this case the presence of
two side handles and the chains may indicate that the object was exhibited
in a treasury when it was not in use liturgically.

The use of a slab of marble for such a very precious object is amply explained by the inscription on the back: "This is not given by the earth since it
is more precious than a gem; it is given by God Himself, from the height
of heaven. As the prophets and the fates and the sacred Sybils tell, the
image of the Virgin is revealed in the little marble". All this, and the
words of the inscription on the front, refer to the legend of Ara Coeli[1],
the Sybil who is supposed to have appeared to Augustus, foretelling the
coming of the Son of God ("Ecce ara primogeniti Dei"). By a miraculous
lusus naturae the veining of the marble has assumed the appearance of the
Madonna and Child, so that the stone becomes more precious than a jewel.
This is not the only known case of such a surprising coincidence: at St.
Sophia in Constantinople they venerated an image of the Madonna and
Child and another with St. John the Baptist, and at San Vitale in Ravenna a
priest in sacred vestments, all visible in the veining of the stone. This also
brings to mind the famous agate cup in the Viennese treasure, on which,
according to the singular interpretation of Lambecius, the name of Christ
could be discerned[2]. The interest in this sort of configuration, halfway between
religion and scientific curiosity, continued to fascinate in the Renaissance
and even in the Baroque period: Aldrovandi, in his *Musaeum Metallicum*
(Bologna, 1648) writes of it at length. It is the manifestation of the spirit of
divine providence in nature itself which becomes a venerated cult object.

The pax is a fine and rare example of Renaissance goldsmith's work, with a highly archaeologising style, typical also of certain aspects of sculpture of the period. Nowadays we might be surprised that, in such a high-class piece, the goldsmith has not bothered to respect the relation between the palmettes of the frames, which are interrupted abruptly at the corners, but this slightly casual, and, we might say now, commercial, characteristic is typical of XVth century Italian goldsmiths' work, and does not preclude the figures of Augustus and the Sybil, the cartouches and the inscriptions being treated with the greatest refinement.

We know nothing of the provenance of this pax: the Medici arms at the top (unusual by the presence of the ivy) are not crowned by the papal tiara, but other votive objects of the Medici popes share this characteristic (Florence, Treasury of S. Lorenzo). In any case it appears most probable that it belongs to the papacy of Leo X (1513–21).

The tribune of the Basilica of Ara Coeli had been frescoed by Pietro Cavallini, as Vasari writes, with the legend of Augustus and the Sybil. In 1517 Leo X granted the title of the Basilica to a cardinal and appointed the first holder[3]. In 1518 a great procession, against the Turks, was held in the same church, during which many relics were exposed. It seems to us very plausible – and no stylistic fact goes against this – that this Pax belongs to these years during which the Ara Coeli was specially venerated. Not long after, indeed, the second Medici Pope, Clement VII, revoked the Basilica's right to a titular cardinal. Paul III overlooked the revocation by Clement VII, and named a cardinal with this title, but it was only under Julius III, in 1551, that the Basilica regained its privileges.

1. C. Hulsen, *The Legend of Ara Coeli,* Rome, 1907.
2. R. Gnoli, *Marmora romana,* Rome, 1971, p. 42. J. von Schlosser, *Raccolte d'arte e di meraviglie,* It. ed. Florence, 1974, p. 112.
3. J. Vester, *L'Ara Coeli, Souvenirs historiques,* Rome, 1886, pp. 51, 64. P. Casimiro, *Memorie istoriche di Ara Coeli,* Rome, 1736, ed. 1845, pp. 518–519.

A. G.-P.

NON·HOC·TERRA·DEDIT·GEMMA·PRETO
SIVS·OMNI
AETHEREA·SVMMVS·MISIT·ABARCE·DEVS
QVAM·VATES·QVAM·FATA·CANVNT·SA
CRAEQ·SYBILLAE
VIRGINIS·EXIGVO·MARMORE·IMAGO
PATET

2   GOLD RING.
    Rome, IInd century A.D.

The hollow hoop expanding to flat bezel set with oval nicolo intaglio of
Bonus Eventus standing facing towards the right holding patera and corn
ears[1].

This type is usually identified with the statue of Bonus Eventus by Euphranor,
mentioned by Pliny, *Natural History*, XXXIV, xix, 77. Bonus Eventus, or
Tripotolemus was the god of the good harvest, and therefore like Ceres, his
female counterpart, especially concerned with agriculture.

1.   For similar see H. B. Walters, *Catalogue of the Engraved Gems and Cameos, Greek,
     Etruscan and Roman in the British Museum,* London, 1926, no. 1768.

Illustration enlarged   D. S.

3   GOLD RING.
    England, XVth century.

Writhen hoop expanding to fluted shoulders engraved with stems of five
petalled flowers and black letter inscription, on one side, *SANS DE*
continued obliquely across the other shoulder *PARTIR*. Rectangular double
ridged bezel engraved with standing figures of the Virgin and Child, and St.
John the Baptist holding the Agnus Dei.
    The inscription which occurs in various spellings on brooches and rings
is a love motto, meaning "without distributing", or "all my love is yours",
the sentiment being emphasised by the accompanying spray of flowers[1].

1.   For a full discussion of English XVth century jewellery thus inscribed see J. Cherry,
     The Medieval Jewellery from Fishpool Nottinghamshire Hoard, a paper read 1st April, 1971
     to the Society of Antiquaries, and published *Archaeologia,* Vol. CIV, including an item
     listed in the inventory of Henry V. Devotional rings of this character which appear to
     be of exclusively English origin are discussed by C. Oman, *British Rings,* London,
     1974, Chapter 7, pp. 54–56.

Illustration enlarged   D. S.

4 GOLD LOCKET RING.

Ring, XVIth century; cameo c. 1500.

The oval hoop terminating in volutes enamelled green, white and lapis blue supporting oval bezel with sides enamelled en suite, and set with a ruby cameo of the Virgin and Child. She is veiled and cradles the Child in one arm, the other is drawn across her breast to clasp His hand outstretched towards her heart. A thumb piece lifts to compass under glass and surrounding dial border engraved with the numbers 1–12[1].

1. For another example of a ruby cameo of this subject see J. Szendrei, *Catalogue Descriptif et Illustré de la Collection de Bagues de Madame Gustave de Tarnoczy*, Paris, 1889, p. 76, Group LV, no. 98, and for other locket rings enclosing compasses see O. M. Dalton, *Catalogue of the Finger Rings, Early Christian Medieval and Later in the British Museum,* London, 1912, nos. 1703, et seq.

Illustration enlarged   D. S.

5 GOLD RING.

c. 1570.

The convex hoop terminating in shoulders with blue and white shields on scrolled red cartouches, the flat bezel in the form of a fleur-de-lys[1] set with five diamonds cut to the shape of petals in collets with scalloped edges outlined in blue enamel, the inside of the shoulders with merchant's marks enamelled en suite. The hoop is damaged.

1. For other rings with the fleur-de-lys as a device, see G. Taylor and D. Scarisbrick, *Finger Rings from Ancient Egypt to the Present Day*, the catalogue of an exhibition held at Goldsmith's Hall, London, and subsequently at the Ashmolean Museum, Oxford, July-September, 1978, nos. 311, 316, 394. F. Falk, *Princely Magnificence,* the catalogue of an exhibition held at the Victoria and Albert Museum, London, October 1980–February 1981, p. 25, discusses diamond lilies recorded from the early XVth century including some presented to Queen Elizabeth.

Illustration enlarged   D. S.

6 GOLD RING.
  Second half of the XVIth century.

The rectangular hoop with black ovolo ornament, terminating in winged shoulders enamelled red and white and set with pairs of table cut diamonds, the high quatrefoil bezel set with a pointed diamond, and the petals similarly set in rectangular collets framed in blue cartouches[1]. The back of the bezel has a pair of fleurs-de-lys enamelled green and lozenges beneath blue ornamental bars linking the volutes above.

1.   For another ring set with five pointed diamonds in similar star-like arrangement see *Catalogue of the Superb Collection of Rings formed by the late Monsieur E. Guilhou*, Sotheby's sale 9th November, 1937, lot 741, also illustrated by E. Fontanay, *Les Bijoux Anciens et Modernes*, Paris, 1887, p. 59.

Illustration enlarged   D. S.

7 GOLD RING.
  Second half of the XVIth century.

The hoop of rectangular section terminating in winged shoulders with red, white and blue enamelled scroll and boss work, the high quatrefoil bezel set with a table cut emerald, the petals with ornament enamelled en suite.

Illustration enlarged   D. S.

8   GOLD GIMMEL RING.
    Germany, XVIth century.

The double hoop terminating in shoulders with blue, red, white and green voltes and H scrolls, the high quatrefoil bezel set with a table cut ruby and diamond, the petals enriched with gold bosses framed in white. Inscription in black Roman capitals on the inner faces of the hoop and bezel *WAS GOT SAMEN FOEGT DAS WIRTEN DIE MENSCHEN NICHT SCHAIDEN* (Matthew 19, v. 6), "What therefore God hath joined together let not man put asunder"[1]. The cut inner faces of the bezel have cavities enclosing enamelled reclining figures, a putto with hour glass and skull, and a demon with cloven hoof and vase spilling green fluid, symbolic of death and sin respectively. The back of the bezel is diapered in black.

According to W. Jones[2], the wedding ring of Martin Luther was also set with a ruby and diamond, emblems of exalted love and fidelity.
    Although the motif of the putto with skull and hour glass occurs in other media as a memento mori[3] it is unusual to find it combined with the demon, though together they provide a clear admonition towards the virtuous life.

1.   For other gimmel (twin) rings with this inscription see Taylor/Scarisbrick, *op. cit.*, no. 712, and O. M. Dalton, *Rings, op. cit.*, no. 991.
2.   W. Jones, *Finger Ring Lore,* London, 1890, p. 483.
3.   F. Parkes Weber, *Aspects of Death in Art*, London, 1914, p. 98, illustrating a bronze statuette with inscription 'Il tempo passa e la morto (sic) ven . . .'

Illustration enlarged   D. S.

9   GOLD GIMMEL RING.
    XVIth century.

The double hoop terminating in shoulders with volute and strap, the high quatrefoil bezel set with a table cut diamond and a ruby, the petals enriched with blue, red and white cruciform ornament. Inscription in black Roman capitals on the inner faces of the hoop and bezel *HOMO PATREM ET MATREM RELINQUET ET ADHERIBIT UXOR,* (Genesis 2, v. 24, "Therefore shall a man leave his father and his mother and shall cleave unto his wife"). Enamelled scrolls ornament the cut inner faces of the bezel above the inscription.

Illustration enlarged   D. S.

10 GOLD RING.
Germany, c. 1600

The rectangular hoop with outer face in white with arches reserved, and boss work, between black faces strung with beads between arches, the inside plain, expanding to shoulders in the form of winged caryatids on bases with volutes each embellished with a girdle set with a table cut ruby, flowing hair, arms clasped across bosom, the head framed in convergent blue scrolls, the broad wings in layers enamelled blue, green and red supporting deep octagonal bezel with white claws above rectangular black panel with foliate scrolls reserved, set with a cabochon sapphire, with two smaller in oval collets above volutes to each side. The back of the bezel is enamelled with green and blue scrollwork framing a pair of red ornamental bars.

Although the sapphire, associated in the lapidaries with chastity and sanctity is customary in episcopal rings and the high proportions suggest some ceremonial purpose this cannot be established in the absence of heraldic or inscribed evidence. However, the quality of the vari-coloured enamelling, together with the fine surface ornament and the modelling of the winged terminal figures represent Renaissance goldwork at its most accomplished, and the ring form may have been chosen as a suitable frame to display the sapphire in some eminent *Kunstkammer* of the time.

Illustration enlarged   D. S.

11 GOLD RING.
Ring c. 1600, cameo later. French control mark, an eagle's head.

The hoop of rectangular section expanding to canted shoulders enamelled black with scrollwork reserved, the sides of high octagonal bezel en suite[1], now set with sardonyx cameo gryllus[2] of four masks conjoined.

1. For signet rings of this type see O. M. Dalton, *Catalogue of the Finger Rings, Early Christian, Byzantine Medieval and Later in the British Museum,* London, 1912, no. 312.
2. For similar cameos see O. M. Dalton, *Catalogue of the Engraved Gems of the Post Classical Periods in the British Museum,* (London, 1915), no. 212, also an imitation of an ancient gem possibly XVIth century. It represents a young woman facing towards the right, her hair merging into the beard of the male head above, of which the hair in turn forms the beard of the head at the back. The neck of the woman merges into a ram's head.

Illustration enlarged   D. S.

12 GOLD RING.
XVIIth century.

The oval hoop with black rectilinear ornament of pairs of slanting bars terminating in red and white winged shoulders with volutes and boss work, the high quatrefoil bezel aslant, and set with a pointed ruby, the petals with white scroll ornament reserved.

Illustration enlarged   D. S.

13   GOLD GIMMEL RING.
     Germany, 1631.

The double hoop terminating in winged shoulders with green, blue and red volutes and strap from which issues hands clasping hearts supporting high box bezel set with a table cut ruby and a diamond. The outer faces of the hoop are inscribed in black Roman capitals *QUOD DEUS CONIUNXIT HOMO NON SEPARABIT* (Matthew 19, v. 6) "What therefore God hath joined together let not man put asunder", and the inner faces with the names *JACOB SIGMUND VON DER SACHSEN MARTHA wurmin*. The cut inner faces of the bezel enclose reclining figures of a baby and a skeleton, symbolic of life and death respectively, the latter with the date 1631 inscribed above. The back of the bezel has a radiate pattern in blue centering on a red sunburst enclosed in white.

The ring is a microcosm of the emblems associated with marriage, being set with a ruby and a diamond, ornamented with hands holding hearts, enclosing miniature skeleton and infant, and inscribed with the names of the partners, the date of the wedding and the Biblical quotation referring to the indissolubility of marriage[1].

1.   For other gimmel rings with similar symbolism see Y. Hackenbroch, *Renaissance Jewellery*, London, 1980, fig. 457, from the Museum of Art, Toledo, and G. Gregorietti, *Jewellery Through the Ages*, London, 1970, p. 198, from the Thyssen Collection, Lugano, though neither of these is inscribed.

D. S.

14   PENDANT JEWEL.
Spain, the central relief XVth century, the frame probably later.

Gold, lozenge shaped pendant, the frame with sunk border set with Gothic
foliage and flowers, enclosing a minute relief of the Adoration of the Kings,
the Virgin seated to the right under a roof supported on a Gothic ruined
building, in front of her, the three Kings with their gifts and, behind, their
followers with a camel. At the base a garnet drop, on each side a cabochon
garnet in tall gold collet, the pendant formed as a dragon's head seizing the
tail of a serpent. The back with a relief panel of flamboyant tracery, the
spandrels chased with Gothic foliage.

    Dimensions: 12.2 × 6.6 cm

Of the few gold objects of this period extant, the nearest is the XVth century
gold salt-cellar from the Trésor de la Couronne de France, now in the
Galerie d'Apollon of the Louvre[1].

1.   R. Lightbown, *Secular Goldsmiths' Work in Medieval France,* London, 1978, pl. 77.

Illustration enlarged   J. H.

15　MINIATURE CASE.
France, c. 1575.
Miniatures: Circle of François Clouet, 1500–1572.

Silver gilt locket set with a miniature of Henri III of France (b. 1551– acc. 1574– d. 1589) wearing the Order of the Saint Esprit on a blue ribbon, ruby set sunburst with pendant in his hair, and an earring, and on the back, a miniature of Louise de Vaudemont, his Queen, whom he married in 1575. She wears a diamond pendant attached to three ropes of pearls, a chain set with sapphires, pearl necklace and earrings, an aigrette and jewelled hair ornaments. Both miniatures are painted on vellum with the back stamped with fleur-de-lys in gold. The glass covers are enclosed in a cable twist border within a frame of silver sections nielloed with scrolls alternating with gilt flutes, suspension ring at the top, simulated pointed diamond at the base. The back of each miniature frame has an outer border nielloed with inscriptions from the Vulgate in Roman capitals: *ISTORUM EST ENIM REGNUM CELORUM* (based on Matthew 5, v. 3 or 10, "For theirs is the kingdom of heaven"), behind the portrait of the king, and *ADDUCENTUR REGI VIRGINES POST EAM* (Vulgate, Psalm 44, v. 15 (Psalm 45, A. V., v. 14) "The virgins her companions that follow her shall be brought unto thee") at the back of the portrait of the Queen. The inner faces of the simulated pointed diamonds are inscribed *R* and *E* (Enricus Rex) respectively, and each miniature is backed by a silver disc held in place by a cable twist border.

Dimensions: 10×6.5 cm

D. S.

16 SCENT BOTTLE.
France, XVIIth century.

Pendant with gold mounts, the body composed of two pieces of turquoise, the lower spherical, the upper of shaped conical form, pearl stopper above, pendant pearl below, on each side of the body a gold lion's mask with pendant pearl, forming the attachment for the chains, which meet in a suspension link with applied gold lion's mask, a third chain connects this link with the stopper.

Dimension: H. 12 cm

Illustration enlarged   J. H.

17 KNIFE AND FORK.
Probably Paris, early XVIIth century.

The handles of heliotrope mounted in gold, of octagonal section, the mounts enamelled with moresques in black and white against a striated gold ground, terminating above in a button finial. The steel knife blade struck with a cutler's mark, a crowned sceptre, probably Dutch, the two pronged fork of gilt bronze.

Dimensions: L. of knife 19 cm; L. of fork 17 cm

Black and white moresques are associated with a Paris workshop, which is believed to have been responsible for the mounts of the onyx ewer, given in 1570 by Charles IX of France to the Archduke Ferdinand of Tyrol, for a bouquet holder and an étui for reading glasses, all enamelled in a similar manner, now in the Kunsthistorisches Museum, Vienna, and also for the mounts of four other vases now divided between the Louvre and the Prado[1].

1.   J. F. Hayward, *Virtuoso Goldsmiths*, London, 1977, pl. 179. Exhibition Catalogue, *Princely Magnificence,* London, Victoria and Albert Museum, 1980, no. 24.

J. H.

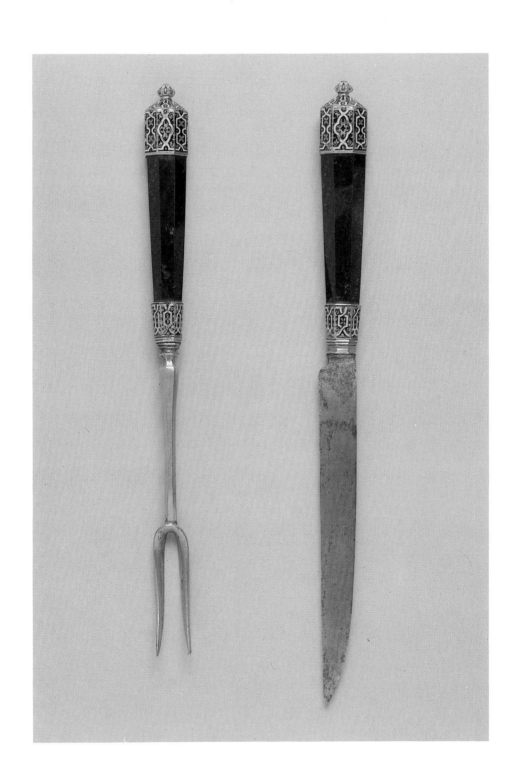

18 KNIFE, FORK AND SPOON.
Prague Imperial Court Workshop, early XVIIth century.

Red jasper mounted in enamelled gold, handles of hexagonal section, the mounts champlevé enamelled white with ovals of translucent green at the intersections, the upper mount terminating above in a figure of a winged harpy, enamelled white and translucent red and green, the lower mount of the knife interrupted by an openwork double cartouche, those of the spoon and fork by a single cartouche-shaped member, the two prongs of the fork also enamelled white and green en suite with the mounts, the knife blade struck with a cutler's mark, a bunch of grapes(?), the jasper spoon bowl with rat-tailed back.

Dimensions: L. of knife 20 cm; of fork 14 cm; of spoon 15 cm

Sets of this type were purely *Kunstkammer* objects, the finials modelled in the round being so delicate as to preclude their practical use. A hardstone spoon in the British Museum (Waddesdon Collection 221) with similar finial is catalogued as French, late XVIth century.

J. H.

19 BOWL OF SPOON.
    South Germany, c. 1600.

Green and pink jasper, the handle of matching stone now missing, the mount
of gold, champlevé enamelled in green and white, the upper face of cartouche
form centering on a translucent blue ovolo.

Dimension: L. 9 cm

J. H.

20 PRESENTOIR.
South Germany, probably Nuremberg, late XVIth century.

Handle of gilt bronze, composed of strapwork enclosing on one side a satyr, and on the other a nude female figure, flanked by cornucopiae and pendant swags, the central part of the handle set with panels of light and dark horn in various checquer patterns. On each side above the blade a lion's mask, broad flat blade with rounded point, the junction of handle and blade masked by pierced strapwork.

   Dimension: L. 40 cm

This Presentoir forms a pair to another in the collection of James de Rothschild at Waddesdon Manor (catalogue no. 185)[1]. The design is derived from the manner of the Nuremberg goldsmith and master of ornament, Matthias Zündt, and is associated with the workshop of Wenzel Jamnitzer of which Zündt was a member. The gilt bronze handle closely resembles the decoration of a series of column-like balance pillars of which examples are in the Cleveland Museum, the Rijksmuseum and the Victoria and Albert Museum. These have been attributed to the Jamnitzer workshop and, more recently, to Hans Epischofer of Nuremberg (fl. c. 1560–90).

1.   C. Blair, *James de Rothschild Collection at Waddesdon Manor,* Fribourg, 1974, p. 429/30.

J. H.

21 LIMOGES ENAMEL PLAQUES.

Jean Poillevé (active c. 1537–1555) (?) and anonymous goldsmith.

The exterior in the form of a binding, the front and back covers of silver, the frame gilt. The spine chased with four panels of Renaissance floral ornament, the front cover set with an arched plaque of a woman nude except for a net, swinging a censer against a landscape background, the Trinity in the sky above, to the right a label inscribed *DIRIGATUR ORŌ MEA SICUT INCENSUM*, (Psalm 140, v. 2), the outer frame engraved with running foliage and in the spandrels above with two putti holding a mass cruet and a chalice respectively. The back cover with arched plaque engraved with an allegorical scene, a label above inscribed *VERI ADORATORES ADORANT SPIRITU* (John 4, v. 23), the outer frame and spandrels above engraved with foliage inhabited by birds.

Within the binding are eight arched plaques each enamelled *en grisaille* and gilt with a devotional subject, as follows:

1. Christ teaching His Apostles. 2. The Almighty appearing to kneeling monks, nuns and peasants. 3. The Dove of the Holy Spirit descending on the Virgin Mary. 4. Christ carrying the Cross to Calvary. 5. A priest preaching to his congregation. 6. Christ healing the sick. 7. The Almighty intervening to save an old man about to be struck by a devil. 8. Christ attending a death-bed scene.

In the lunette above each subject is a phrase from the Lord's Prayer on a shield supported by two cherubs. The first plaque is inscribed in the lunette (in translation), 'When you pray do not do so at length as do the infidels but pray as follows'. The first two shields are signed M.G., the first plaque is signed at the bottom K.I.

Dimensions of the cover: 8.3 × 9 cm

The monogrammist K.I., who usually signed KIP, has been tentatively identified with Jean Poillevé, a goldsmith and enameller, who is mentioned in documents dated 1537 and 1555. His work is represented in the Walters Art Gallery, Baltimore, by nine plaques representing religious and secular subjects[1].

The silver case, though made for and contemporary with the enamel plaques, may not be of French origin. The engraved subjects appear to derive from Dutch or German sources, thus the scene of Christ and the Woman of Samaria is related to Dirick Vellert's engraving of this subject, which is dated 1523 (Popham, P. C. Q., XII, p. 366, no. 6), whereas the border of the back cover is apparently derived from Virgil Solis (O'Dell-Franke, nos. g. 49–76). For the mounting of limoges enamels by German goldsmiths, compare the Limoges enamel ewer and basin[2] by Pierre Reymond and Leonard Limousin mounted in Nuremberg, probably by Wenzel Jamnitzer in the Schatzkammer der Residenz, Munich, nos. 568/9.

1. For a list of works of this prolific master, see P. Verdier, *Catalogue of Painted Enamels of the Renaissance,* Walters Art Gallery, nos. 72/80.
2. Illustrated in Rosenberg, *Jamnitzer,* Frankfurt am Main, 1920.

J. H.

22 PLAQUE.
Netherlands, XVIth century.

Silver, parcel-gilt, the circular central panel with an applied three-quarters relief of a bishop (St. Sylvester?) holding a book in his left hand, a key in his right, standing on a dragon, flanked on each side by a heraldic shield, (quarterly, sable a lion rampant or) and by the initials *PH*; the outer frame of concave section, with the monogram of the letters *PH* alternating with winged cherub's heads; at the central point below, the name *BERGHE* in letters applied separately.

The central panel struck on the back with the mark of the City of Louvain, a key and a third mark (presumably of the maker) a ciborium.

Diameter: 13 cm

While this plaque corresponds both in form and in dimensions to a morse for securing a cope, it seems to have had some other purpose. The back is fitted with two slotted staples, a third now missing, for attachment to some wood or metal base, perhaps a coffin, casket or reliquary. Four holes pierced in the outer border appear to be later alterations. The arms are Netherlandish and probably of a city or town. There is a village of Berg north-east of Brussels.

J. H.

23 CASKET.
Italy, early XVIth century.

Silver gilt, rectangular with spiral colonettes at the corners, each surmounted by a lion sejant, the four sides with applied geometrical patterns in filigree and twisted wire work, the four feet with applied figures of geese facing respectively sinister and dexter, in the centre of the front a nielloed medallion with a coat of arms with putto supporters, the cover of hipped form, divided into compartments by twisted wire borders, in the centre, a wirework medallion.

The nielloed medallion, though contemporary, was apparently once attached to another object.

Dimensions: 14×8×9.5 cm

A similar casket in the British Museum (Waddesdon Collection, no. 220) with filigree of more delicate form is catalogued as South Italian and XVIIth century.

J. H.

39

24 TANKARD.
Salzburg, c. 1550.

Silver, parcel gilt, the barrel inset with cast and chased panels illustrating King Solomon, David with the head of Goliath, Gideon, Samson and the lion[1], divided by engraved moresque ornament, inscriptions recording the scenes above the moulded base, another at the rim, the lid inset with four cast medallions alternating with engraved mauresques, the loop handle with similar decoration. The inscription at the lip reads: *PROPTER CRAPVLAM. MVLTI. OBIERVNT. QVI. AVTEM. ABSTINENS. EST. ADJICIET. VITAM. ECLE* 37 (taken from *Ecclesiasticus* 37, v. 31).

Dimension: H. 10.5 cm

1. Similar panels are illustrated by Ingrid Weber, *Deutsche, Niederländische und Französiche Renaissanceplaketten*, 1500–1650, Munich, 1975, no. 616, 1, 2, 3, 4, plate 169.

J. H.

25 TANKARD.
Southern Germany, last quarter of the XVIth century.

The silver-gilt barrel cast with panels of interlacing strapwork enclosing female terms flanked by satyrs and sphinxes, probably after models from the workshop of Wenzel Jamnitzer, separated by oval cartouches, engraved with foliage portrait busts after Virgil Solis[1], the cover also matching and centred by a medallion, with identical thumbpiece and handle, the base stamped above the foot with a repeating die of overlapping foliate scrolls. Unmarked except for XIXth century French control marks, probably Augsburg, c. 1575.

Dimension: H. 12 cm

The portrait medallion is that of Jan Pan Jaroslaw Waranowski von Waldeck, 1534, designed by Severin Brachmann. For details of the portrait busts see Ilse O'Dell-Franke[2]. The original engravings are inscribed 'IVDEA, SOFEA'.

1. Georg Habich, *Die Deutschen Schaumünzen des XVI Jahrhunderts*, Munich, 1934, Vol. 2, no. 3255, plate CCVIII, no. 1.
2. Ilse O'Dell-Franke, *Kupferstiche und Radierungen aus der Werkstatt des Virgil Solis*, Wiesbaden, 1977, no. h67, plate 97.

J. H.

26 TANKARD.
Germany, first quarter of the XVIIth century.

Silver-gilt, the drum embossed with foliate scrollwork, enclosing three oval cartouches chased with figures of officers and soldiers after or in the manner of prints by Jacob de Gheyn after Henrick Goltzius, as follows:
from the left to right an officer[1], a musketeer[2], and a pikeman[3], cherub thumbpiece, the handle engraved with naturalistic flowers, shield terminal from which the original owner's arms have been erased.

Dimension: H. 26 cm

1. For a warrior seen from the back, compare the print, Strauss no. 159 of 1582, engraved by Goltzuis.
2. Hollstein no. 359.
3. Based on Goltzius' portrait of a pike-bearer of 1583, but with a different head, Strauss no. 166.

Anonymous Loan.   J. H.

27 RELIEF OF THE EMPEROR CHARLES V.
South German, probably Nuremberg, c. 1600.

Cast and chased silver, of architectural form enclosing within an arched niche, an applied figure of the Emperor, his hand resting on a shield charged with the Habsburg arms (the Bindenschild).

Dimension: H. 9.4 cm

This plaque is the central feature of a group of silver and silvered metal mounts from a jewel casket, though more recently they were mounted on a miniature tabernacle. Comparable cast figures are found on caskets from the workshop of Matthias Wallbaum of Nuremberg and of that of Boas Ulrich of Augsburg[1], but other detached figures showing considerable resemblance to this relief have been convincingly attributed to Christoph Jamnitzer (1563–1618)[2], the last goldsmith member of the famous Nuremberg family. Such figures or sets of mounts for caskets were cast in numbers and sold separately to ébénistes who manufactured the elaborately decorated cabinets that were an essential feature of the princely Kunstkammer.

1. R. Löwe, *Die Augsburger Goldschmiedwerkstatt des Matthias Walbaum*, Munich, 1975, nos. 43–56 (Wallbaum), nos. 97–99 (Boas Ulrich).
2. E. Kris and O. von Falke, "Beitrage zu den Werken Christoph und Hans Jamnitzer", *Jahrbuch der Preussischen Kunstsammlungen*, Vol. 47, 1926, p. 196 ff.

J. H.

28 TABLE CENTRE. GUSTAVUS ADOLPHUS, KING OF SWEDEN.
Hamburg, Heinrich Lambrecht III, XVIIth century.

Silver, parcel gilt, the oval base chased with grotesque masks and supported
on four ball feet with floral escutcheons, the top chased with rocks and grass,
applied figures of lizards and a frog, within the base a clockwork with bell
covered by an oval plate pierced and engraved with a vase of flowers.
Arising from the base a prancing horse with gilt trappings and the figure of
Gustavus Adolphus with marshall's staff in his right hand, reins in his left,
sword at his side. The head of horse and figure wrought separately and
removable, the figure partly wrought and partly cast, the lace collar, skirt
and sash detachable. The base struck with the Hamburg town mark and
maker's mark of Heinrich Lambrecht the second.

Dimension: H. 42 cm

An almost identical equestrian figure of Gustavus Adolphus was made by
the Augsburg goldsmith, David Schwestermuller c. 1645–50[1]. A design for
this group by Hans Schorer of Augsburg in the Nationalmuseum, Stockholm,
was used by David Schwestermuller in the production of his piece which
cost 260 Reichstaler.

1. H. Seling, *Die Kunst der Augsburge-Goldschmiede,* Vol. II, pl. 587.

J. H.

29 GILT-METAL, SILVER AND ENAMEL CASKET.
Southern Germany, in the manner of Boas Ulrich, first quarter of the
XVIIth century.

Of tiered rectangular form, applied in silver with scroll panels, masks hung
with rings and terminal figures, raised on caryatid supports, the base with
pierced panels of Renaissance ornament, fitted with a drawer, the doors of
the central section opening to reveal an enamel plaque decorated with
flowers and fruit below a canopy above another drawer, the upper hinged
compartment chased at the angles, with an inner cover and lock in the
manner of Michel Mann, surmounted by a figure in a horse-drawn chariot,
apparently a later addition.

    Dimension: H. 20.5 cm

The enamel plaque is related to the work of David Altenstetter (c. 1547–
1617)[1]. The casket and its mount are similar to other examples by Boas
Ulrich, who was much influenced by the Walbaum workshop[2]. The design
of the inner drawer is based on engravings by Virgil Solis[3].

1.   For a biographical note see Exhibition Catalogue of the Schröder Collection, *Virtuoso
   Goldsmith's Work from the age of Humanism,* London, 1979, no. 36.
2.   For a biographical reference and examples of his work see Regina Löwe, *Die Augsburger Goldschmiedwerkstatt des Matthias Walbaum*, Munich, 1975. Biographical note
   pp. 20–21, examples of his work no. 98a.v, plate 106, no. 99a, plate 107.
3.   Ilse O'Dell-Franke, *Kupferstiche und Radierungen aus der Werkstatt des Virgil Solis,*
   Wiesbaden, 1977, no. g70–72, plate 82.

J. H.

30 PAIR OF CANDLESTICKS.
Danzig, maker's mark, the initials A.M. of Andrew Mackensen (c. 1600–1670).

Silver, with baluster stems, nozzles cast with a bull's head in relief, knurled drip pans, the spreading bases engraved with the same arms 'Wieniawa' surmounted by a coronet and an ecclesiastical hat with six tassels on each side, and at the sides the initials V.C.D.L.D.G.EP.VS.

Dimensions: H. 21.5 cm × 18.5 cm

The initials stand for Venceslaus, Comes De Leszno, Dei Gratia, Episcopus Varmiensis. Venceslaus de Leszno Leszczynski (1605–1666) was appointed first private secretary to Sigismund III, King of Poland in 1629 and in the following year Secretary of the Realm. In 1644 he was created Bishop of Warmia (Ermland), a position which he held until 1658 when he was appointed Archbishop of Gniezno and Primate of the Realm. Stanizlas Leszczynski, King of Poland and Duke of Lorraine in the latter part of the XVIIIth century, was a member of the same family.

Andrzej (as he was called in Poland) Mackensen (c. 1600–1670) was one of the leading goldsmiths of his time. Of Scottish parentage, he first worked in Cracow, where in 1628 he was appointed Royal Goldsmith. He subsequently moved to Torun and finally to Danzig where he settled in 1643. He was several times Warden of the Guild and his considerable output of silver was mostly commissioned by the Polish court, the Church and the aristocracy.

Anonymous Loan   J. H.

31 SET OF THREE SPOONS.
Danzig, Constantin Hein and the master HP, second half of the XVIIth century.

Silver-gilt, the knops in the form of nude female terms, rectangular, partly chamfered stems, the bowls engraved with the arms of von der Linda and the initials A.V.D.L.

Dimension: L. 20.5 cm

The family of von der Linda was descended from a dignitary of the Deutsches Ritter Orden. Having their seat in East Prussia, they had by the XVIth century become Polish. This type of spoon, sometimes with mottoes engraved along the stem, was popular in the XVIth and XVIIth centuries in Poland and the Baltic area.

Anonymous Loan   J. H.

32 SILVER AQUAMANILE.
Danzig, c. 1650.
The maker's mark, a bird, is unidentified.

A silver ewer in the form of a winged Cupid with a bow and arrows, riding a lion, on domed base chased with rocks and plants, scrolled feet, with its original leather case.

Dimensions: 30 × 18 × 27 cm

This is a particularly unusual and spendidly decorative Baroque object, which shows the fantasy and high quality of Danzig goldsmiths to the best advantage. It goes back in its fundamental shape and usage to similar vessels produced in German-speaking centres since the Romanesque period. They were particularly popular in such centres as Augsburg and Nuremberg during the XVIth century. The brio and liveliness of design and execution of this piece place it amongst the finest products of Danzig silver in the XVIIth century.

L. d'U.

THREE VENETIAN SARACENIC BOWLS.
Late XVth/early XVIth century.

A. and B. are in gilt bronze, of cylindrical form on a stand, decorated with arabesques and rosettes of geometrical and naturalistic derivation, C. is in bronze, of cylindrical form with two caryatid lions forming the handle; all three are decorated with designs of arabesques, plant and geometric motifs inlaid with silver.

> Dimensions: A. H. 12.2 cm; Diam. 16.2 cm
> B. H. 12.2 cm; Diam. 15 cm
> C. H. 10 cm; Diam. 26 cm

According to the great historian of Venice, Pompeo Molmenti, "among the metalwork industries, that of vases and chased vessels made by the Saracens . . . was soon accepted and flourished in an Oriental city such as Venice . . . Oriental craftsmen, particularly Arabian ones, taught the Venetians, from whose workshops there emerged [all sorts of artefacts] of most gracious forms with arabesques, inlaid with lines and stippled. The name of a XVIth century Levantine artist is often seen engraved on [these vessels]: that of Mahmud Al Kurdi, who must have come from the Kurdish region near the Euphrates and who was almost an heir to the Mesopotamian metalwork traditions"[1]. The technique that we see in these three bowls couldn't be better explained (the same author reproduced some of these items including the extraordinary *vieilleuse* in the Louvre and a piece signed by Mahmud Al Kurdi in the Victoria and Albert Museum: no. 78, 12.30.705, with the inscription "engraved by the master Mahmud Al Kurdi who hopes to be forgiven").

If most of these decorative objects bear a strictly orientalising decoration, number C has the rare quality of mixing Oriental and Occidental motifs (the handle). The influence of this type of Islamic decoration was paramount in Venice during the late XVth and early XVIth centuries: this is specially obvious in book bindings of the period but it may be of interest to note that even a great artist such as Vittore Carpaccio was not indifferent to it: the pedestals of S. Anastasia and of S. Simeon of his polyptych in Zara are decorated with this sort of motif[2].

More recent research has shown that this type of metalwork was not only typical of Venice. It appears that some Muslims were also active in other Italian cities like Florence or Pisa. It seems also possible that Italian craftsmen who had learnt their art in the Orient were active in Italy using a technique that cannot always be easily distinguished from that of their Eastern colleagues. Indeed A and B were altered, although it is not obvious at first sight: the supports which hold the bowls in place are certainly not by the same hand that made the upper parts. It appears plausible that these were made in Europe although not much later than the bowls themselves: the quality is almost as good.

It will be noticed finally that this type of object is often mentioned in the Medicean inventories of the Renaissance. It has been possible even to

c

identify some of these items which are still preserved in the Museo Nazionale in Florence[3].

1. P. Molmenti *La Storia di Venezia nelle vita privata dalle origini alla caduta della repubblica*, Bergamo (7th edition), 1928, pp. 142 and 147.
2. G. Fiocco, *Carpaccio,* Paris, 1931, plates XVIII and XIX.
3. W. L. Hildburgh, "Dianaderie ewers with Venetian-Saracenic decorations", *The Burlington Magazine*, LXXIX, 1941, pp. 17-22; H. Huth, "Sarazenen in Venedig?", *Festschrift für Heinz Ladendorf,* edited by P. Bloch and G. Zich, Cologne, 1970; M. Spellanzani, "Metalli islamici", *Le Arti del Principato Mediceo*, Florence, 1980.

Anonymous Loan   A. G.-P.

a

b

34 CASKET.
France, mid XVIth century.

Silver and gilt bronze, rectangular with arched top, the silver sides engraved with moresques, the corner mounts formed as pilasters with cherub's head capitals, the lock strap finely engraved with floral scrolls introducing masks and figures, the combination lock retaining its original key with handle cast and chased as a putto holding a shield. Applied to the body of the casket are ten circular or oval medallions cast and chased with busts of a Roman Emperor (twice), Diana (twice), Minerva, and male and female heads in contemporary costume.

Dimensions: 18 × 11 × 11 cm

A similar casket, but with steel body covered with velvet, is in the Victoria and Albert Museum (inv. no. 3627/56). The combination lock opens on the word HENRI, confirming the attribution to France. The existence of a number of similar caskets, but with Limoges enamels instead of steel panels, proves the French origin of this and of the succeeding casket[1].

1. For a Limoges enamel casket with mounts of the same design, see P. Verdier, *Catalogue of the Painted Enamels of the Renaissance,* Walters Art Gallery, Baltimore, 1967, no. 45, p. 92/4.

J. H.

35 STEEL CASKET.
France, mid XVIth century.

Wood lined, rectangular with arched lid, mounts of gilt bronze, the corner mounts formed as pilasters with winged cherub's head capitals, the combination lock in the form of a projecting buttress, the key surmounted by a Harpy.

The steel panels etched with scenes as follows:
Front (left): Judith dining with Holophernes; (right): Judith decapitating Holophernes while his guard sleeps.
Back: Knights in combat in front of a castle (re-etched).
Left-hand side (above): Judith on the way to the camp of Holophernes; (below): Judith returning with the head of Holophernes.
Right-hand side (above): Judith setting out with her mother; (below): King receiving a knight in an encampment outside a city wall.
Cover (front): Combat between mounted men in costume of the first half of the XVIth century; (rear): Mounted men setting forth from a walled city.

Dimensions: 17×11.5×11 cm

For the form of the lock, see note to catalogue no. 34.

J. H.

36 GILT COPPER MINIATURE CASKET.
Southern Germany, Michel Mann (active c. 1589 and 1630).

The top and sides engraved with half-length figures of men and women in costume of the first half of the XVIIth century, the base engraved with a bunch of fruit, the whole enclosed in a silver framework, the central strap at the top signed by the maker, Michel Mann.

Dimensions: 4×7 cm

Michel Mann, locksmith[1], is recorded c. 1589 in Augsburg and worked later in Nuremberg, he died after 1630 in Wöhrd. He specialised in making miniature cannon and pistols as well as caskets, the latter often silver mounted. His practice of signing his name in full was unusual at the time.

1.   W. D. Wixon, *Renaissance Bronzes from Ohio Collections,* Cleveland, 1975, catalogue no. 191.

J. H.

37 A WROUGHT AND CHISELLED IRON CASKET.
Germany, dated 1733. Johann Gottlieb Dittman of Hirschberg.

The front of the casket is applied with figures of classical warriors with spears, set between Corinthian pilasters. The ends bear lion masks with ring handles and are also between Corinthian pilasters. The lid is applied with a keyhole escutcheon and, at the corners, with four seated dachshunds. The interior of the lid has an intricate locking mechanism of twenty-six bolts which still functions perfectly. Over this is a gilt pierced and elaborately worked cover which bears two engraved cartouches with the names of the maker and designer as follows:

Inventirt von Sigmund Gatchenhauer Stadt Schlosser und bey dem selben zu einem Meister Stück gemacht worden von Johann Gottlieb Dittman Schlosser Gesell von Hirschberg gebürtig. Anno 1733.

These inscriptions record that the chest was the masterpiece of Johann Gottlieb Dittman, journeyman locksmith of Hirschberg (between Nuremberg and Leipzig) and made in the workshop of and designed by Sigmund Gatchenhauer, blacksmith to the city.

The casket rests on an original gilt iron stand pierced with eagles, flowers and scrolling acanthus foliage.

Dimensions: L. 87 cm; W. 47 cm; H. 52 cm

Masterpieces of this type were not commissioned, but had to be made by the aspirant to admission as master at his own expense. When it was difficult to find a purchaser, such pieces were offered as a gift to a local prince or nobleman, who, if he accepted it, would be bound to offer an appropriate gratuity.

A wrought iron masterpiece coffer in the Victoria and Albert Museum is of much smaller proportions. This example must be one of the most lavish and complex ever made.

J. H.

SCIENTIFIC INSTRUMENTS,
WATCHES AND CLOCKS

---

38 A GILT METAL BOX COMPENDIUM.
German, attributed to Erasmus Habermehl, c. 1600.

Dimension: 88 mm square

The upper surface of one of the sides engraved with the days of the week and corresponding planetary scales within two twelve-hour periods, the centre with revolving disc with apertures for the day of the age and phase of the moon, the corners with engraved decoration, the inner surface with anastrolabic dial for the conversion of planetary hours, the centre with pewter universal sundial with hinged chapter ring with Roman numerals above an inset glazed compass and usable for latitudes, 42–54 degrees, the underside of the compass rose engraved with a classical portrait of a warrior, the inner surface of the second gilt cover engraved with a list of towns and their latitudes, the upper surface with a quadrant, plumb lacking.

Erasmus Habermehl (died 1606), was the *Astronomischer und Geometrischer Instrumentenmacher* to the Emperor Rudolf II in Prague.

J. H.

Eleuation

Paris 48
Rouan 49
Lion 45
Toulouze 43
Bourdeaux 44
Poictiers 47
Nantes 48
Diion 45
Auignon 43
Marseille 43

Romme
Naples 42
Milan 40
Turin 45
Anuers 45
Londres 50
Lisbonne 53
Ciuille 37
Tolede 37
40
Caragose 42

69

39 COMPENDIUM.
French, dated 1611.

Gilt metal of box form, the upper surface of the front cover with rotating alidade, turning above a scale of degrees and named compass points, the corners decorated with scrolling foliage, inhabited by birds, the underside of the lid with twenty place names and their latitudes, the centre with glazed compass with engraved scales and named points, set in a plate finely engraved with floral decoration, hinged above is a sundial for equal hours with swivelling gnomon, the upper surface of the lower cover with nocturnal and folding pointer, disc for the age of the moon and scales for hours and months of the year, the corners engraved with grotesque birds, the inside of the cover with dial with Roman numerals and scales for seven latitudes, inscribed *Fait par le Sieur du Ferrier l'an 1611, Novemb. 21*, folding latitude scale for the string gnomon, the band engraved with scrolling foliage, the whole suspended from a loose ring.

Dimensions: 8 × 9 cm

Several watchmakers of the Ferrier family are recorded in Paris in the XVIIth century. Two of them, Antoine and his son, Guillaume, were awarded the privilege of *Logement* in the Galerie du Louvre. Both were clockmakers to Louis XIII.

J. H.

40 PENDANT WATCH.
Nevers, Abraham Cusin, early XVIIth century.

Silver and gilt metal wrought in the form of the badge of the Order of the
St. Esprit, the applied silver band decorated with engraved scrolling foliage,
both silver covers centred with applied blue enamelled gold doves, the one
on the front surrounded by the Emblems of the Evangelists, that on the
back with angels, the bezels decorated with cherubim, scrolling foliage and
the Instruments of the Passion, the inside of the covers gilt, the front
engraved with the Annunciation, the back with the Nativity, the gilt-metal
dial panel engraved with reclining figures and rabbits, the applied gilt-metal
chapter ring engraved with the Adoration of the Magi, the verge movement
formed to fit the case with eight triangular pierced pillars, fusee with gut,
the balance cock pierced with an irregular edged floral pattern, the pendant
in the form of addorsed dolphins, pendant from the original rose-twist ring.

Diameter: 4.5 cm

Abraham Cusin was working in Nevers in 1593 to 1666. This is a watch
of exceptional quality and was most probably made to order to mark a
special occasion. It is also unusual to find such a watch being made in a
relatively unknown centre. It could well have been produced as a special
order, perhaps for John Casimir, one time King of Poland, who returned
to the Abbeys of Nevers and St. Germain des Près after his abdication.

J. H.

41 PENDANT WATCH.
Amsterdam. Reynier Passchier, early XVIIth century.

Oval case of silver and gilt metal, the front cover engraved with Andromeda,
the back with Aeneas rescuing Anchises from Troy, within foliate scrollwork
borders, the inside of the front cover engraved with an officer and his lady
in contemporary costume; the inside of the front with a couple making
music, the band engraved en suite, silver dial engraved with a figure of
Chronos and foliate scrolls, gilt brass chapter ring, single hand. The backplate signed *Reynier Passchier à Amsterdam*, brass verge movement with
pierced, engraved and gilt balance cock, steel verge.

Dimension: H. 3.2 cm

L. d'U.

42 PENDANT WATCH.
Lyon, Hughes Combret, c. 1581 to 1622.

The enamelled gold case of tulip bud form, the three petals champlevé and cloisonné enamelled with tulips and naturalistic flowers in translucent colours against a white ground, gold chapter ring with black numerals, the hand formed as a snake. Original verge movement, signed *Hughes Combret a Lyon*, gut driven fusee, ratchet wheel regulator, steel balance wheel, pierced and engraved cock.

Dimension: H. including ring pendant, 5 cm

Hughes Combret, born Egletons, worked in Lyon c. 1581 to his death in 1622. The case was probably made in Geneva.

J. H.

43 PENDANT WATCH.
France (?), first half of the XVIIth century.

The gold case of tulip bud form, champlevé enamelled in translucent colours against a white ground, each of the petals with a central reserved area of cloisonné enamel of conventional floral design, the dial champlevé enamelled against a red translucent red ground, gold chapter ring with black numerals, gold hand in form of a lizard.

Original verge movement with gut driven fusee, steel balance wheel, ratchet wheel regulator, pierced and engraved cock, the backplate with space left blank for signature.

Dimension: H. including suspension ring, 5 cm

A similar watch in the Victoria and Albert Museum (no. 785–1901) has the movement signed J. H. Ester, who is believed to have worked in Geneva. The fact that the backplate has been left blank for signature suggests that the movement was made in a large centre, probably Geneva, and sold to a French watchmaker for completion and signature.

J. H

42   43

44 PENDANT WATCH.
London, John Willowe, c. 1620–30.

Cruciform silver and gilt metal case, the front and back covers engraved with the Immaculata and the Crucifixion respectively, the band with flowers and scrollwork, silver dial engraved with the Resurrection, the Vernicle, Supper at Emmaus, gilt chapter ring, blued steel hand, gilt backplate, pinned balance cock, pierced and engraved with flowers and an acorn, ratchet set-up with scrolling pierced tail, verge movement, baluster pillars, chain-driven fusee. Signed on the backplate Jo WILLOWE IN FLEESTRE.

Dimension: L. 6.2 cm

John Willowe, apprenticed 1609, admitted Blacksmith's Company, London, 1617, warden of Clockmaker's Company, 1632, Master, 1635. A signed watch by this maker is in the British Museum.

J. H.

45 PENDANT WATCH.
Turkey, second half XVIIth century.

Oval, the gilt metal case decorated with a diaper of flowers set alternately against white and black ground, the band with flowers in low relief. The dial plate covered with pierced and engraved floral tracery, silver chapter ring with Turkish numerals and touch pieces of seed pearls (some lacking), the backplate with similar tracery, pierced and engraved balance cock, steel balance, regulator dial with Arabic numerals, signed in Arabic letters, the verge movement with gut driven fusee, elaborate pierced pillars.

Dimension: H. 6.5 cm

J. H.

46 FALLING BALL CLOCK.
German, late XVIIth century.

Signed on movement Hans Schlemmer. The brass case in the form of a sphere
with an applied Roman chapter-ring at the equator and an engraved ring
with Arabic numerals, the silvered single hand in the form of a putto, showing
the time simultaneously on both chapter-rings. One-day verge movement
with fusee and cat gut. Wound by lifting the ball.

L. d'U.

47 CARRIAGE CLOCK.
Poland, Isaac Angot, late XVIIth century.

The verge movement signed on the backplate *ANGOT HORLOGEUR DU ROY A ZAMOSC*; three trains, going, striking and alarum. Silver dial, the chapter ring with black numerals, the inner dial serves the alarum. Steel balance wheel, pierced brass balance cock. The inner case with four groups of perforations for alarum and striking, the outer case missing.

Diameter: 10 cm

The maker is presumably identical with Isaac Angot, a French Huguenot, recorded as working in Amsterdam in the late XVIIth century. He is known to have had patrons in Central and Eastern Europe, but there is no other record of his having worked in Zamosc. The signature on the movement gives rise to an interesting hypothesis. Marie Casimire de la Grange d'Arquien (1641–1716) was first married to the wealthy Count John Zamoyski (1627–1665), Palatine of Sandomierz and Lord of Zamosc. Though she was brought up in Poland at the court of the French-born Queen Marie Louise Gonzaga de Nevers, she was of French origin and in her travels abroad may have come in contact with Angot and invited him to set up in Zamosc, which was a flourishing town. If this is so, it would have been natural for her, following her second marriage in 1665 to John Sobieski, the future King John III of Poland, to obtain for Angot the title of *Horloger du Roi*. This could have taken place after 1674 when Sobieski was elected King of Poland.

J. H.

48 TABERNACLE CLOCK.
Germany, first half of XVIIth century.

Tower case of gilt metal in five stages, the base of ogee profile with four
pierced panels containing a Renaissance vase within interlacing strapwork,
the movement within rectangular stage with four projecting corner pilasters
engraved with overlapping scale ornament, the sides set with recessed
pierced arched panels of floral scrolls enclosing birds and animals, the front
with applied Roman chapter ring and inner ring with Zodiacal signs,
subsidiary dial below showing the quarters, the steel hands apparently later,
the two dials of silver enriched with polychrome champlevé floral enamel,
the back with subsidiary dial, now unfunctional, the front and back engraved
en suite with the sides; the upper stages containing the bell, pierced and
engraved with birds amidst scrollwork and with portrait medallions alternating with vases surmounted by a pillared gallery enclosing a warrior, above
this a domed roof supporting an openwork obelisk enclosed within an
armillary sphere, the whole with turned vase finials. Later English eight-day
movement with anchor escapement, half-hour striking.

Dimension: 64 cm

J. H.

49   NIGHT CLOCK.
     Rome, second half of the XVIIth century.

Signed on the back of the movement: *JOSEPH CAMPANUS INVENTOR ROMA*. Architectural case in ebony and ebonised wood in the form of a portico with double Corinthian columns with gilt bronze capitals and other ornaments. The oil painting on the quadrant panel shows the Four Seasons in a boat guided by Time; a young flying putto holds a scroll with the inscription *TV DORMIIS ET TEMPVS TVVM NAVIGAT*, which is taken from St. Ambrose and refers to the sleeping young man below him. On the back an allegory of Death. Inside of the case the original tin candle holder.

     Dimensions: 120 × 81 × 32 cm

The message which the painting is designed to convey is clear. Mention should be made of a similar clock with an almost identical composition, but in reverse: both these compositions and their execution can be ascribed to Carlo Maratti, who painted some clock dials for the Roman aristocratic families[1]. It may be important to recall here a quotation from Chantelou's *Journal du voyage du Bernin en France en 1665*: "*Son Eminence* (Cardinal Antonio Barberini) *a fait voir au Cavalier* (Bernini) *une montre pour la nuit où, par le moyen d'une lampe qui éclaire le cadron, on peut voir à toute heure de la nuit quelle heure il est. Il y a dans cette montre un tableau de Carlo Maratte, de petites figures d'un pied de haut que le Cavalier a fort louées*". This clock was presented to Louis XIV by the Cardinal, and the King was sufficiently pleased with it to have some ornaments added to the ebony case. It is not certain whether the clock in question still exists but the one exhibited here does indeed have some bronze ornaments which have been added to it, as will be demonstrated below. In the Rijksmuseum, Amsterdam, there exists a drawing for a clock dial which is inscribed "di Carlo Maratti Roma"; the eminent historian of Italian clocks, E. Morpurgo, has published this drawing accepting this inscription without query. Even though this attribution has been doubted it is clear that Maratti was responsible for similar decorations[2]. Regarded as a piece of furniture, the clock is almost certainly the work of one of the various German *ebénistes* who were active in Rome during the second half of the XVIIth century. As has been stated elsewhere the most impressive example of this sort of furniture is the *studiolo* (cabinet) in Vienna, made by Giacomo Herman who signed it in Rome in 1668. This contains a night clock, not very different from ours, signed by Pietro Tommaso, brother of Giuseppe Campani, and dated 1663. Herman is known to have been at the Palace of the Pope on the Quirinal on the 7th of July, 1670, to repair a night clock ("*per incollare alcune cornici dello studiolo dell'horologio della morte*"). While it is an established fact that Herman collaborated with at least one of the Campani, other cabinet makers, like the Swiss Giovanni Sigrist and the German Giovanni Falghero (Falker) are also known to have been active in the same city at that period.

The technical aspects of *orologi della morte* (death clocks), *orologi notturni* (night clocks) or *orologi muti* (dumb clocks) has been discussed at length in specialised publications[4]. It seems that they were invented with the intention of not disturbing the insomniac Pope Alexander VII (Chigi, 1655–1667), who wanted to be able to see the exact time during the night.

It still remains uncertain whether Giuseppe or Pietro Tommaso Campani was the inventor of this type of clock. Giuseppe Campani was not only a clockmaker but also a prolific writer. In 1660 in Rome he published a *Discourse* on his dumb clock which he claimed to have invented, but in the same year his brother published a *Letter* on the same subject making the same claim. Giuseppe was also a gifted maker of scientific and optical instruments, some of which were acquired by the Landgraf von Hesse and are in the Landesmuseum in Cassel, while other examples are in Dresden. Among his signed clocks, which are similar to the present example, although none is of such grandiose dimensions, there is one with Jacob's Dream painted on the dial which bears an identical signature on the movement and has a very similar case. The only difference is that the example exhibited has various gilt bronze embellishments – two putti and a Venus, the latter after a well-known antique prototype; these were added afterwards, still in the XVIIth century however, as the passage in Chantelou's diary quoted above suggests[5].

1. A. González-Palacios, "Avvio allo studio della mobilia romana" (Introduction to G. Lizzani's *Il Mobile romano*, Milan, 1970, plate XXX.
2. A. González-Palacios, "Bernini as a Furniture Designer", *The Burlington Magazine*, no. 812, vol. CXII, November, 1970, p. 719. This article contains other bibliographical information.
3. See Note 1.
4. E. Morpurgo, *Dizionario degli orologiai italiani,* Milan, 1974, ad vocem; E. Morpurgo, "Un orologio di Pietro Tommaso Campani", *La Clessidra*, XXIV, December, 1968, no. 12; G. Brusa, *L'arte dell'Orologeria in Europa,* Milan, 1978, p. 118.
5. Other works by Giuseppe Campani are, according to Morpurgo, in Dresden, Cassel, the Del Vecchio Collection in Milan, S. Bedini's collection in U.S.A. and the Spanish Embassy in Rome. Morpurgo (*Dizionario*) reproduces the clock with Jacob's Dream of which there is a good colour reproduction in A. Simoni, *Orologi italiani*, Milan, 1965, p. 136. Some similar clocks are reproduced by Brusa, *op. cit.,* plates 313–314, 407/408 (this author often ignores the previous bibliography concerning clocks as pieces of furniture).

A. G.-P.

50 MANTEL CLOCK.
Clock, Paris, third quarter of the XVIIth century.
Plaque, Florence, early XVIIth century.

Case: Ebony, with tortoiseshell and *pietra dura* inlay (in the pediment, forming a picture of The Prodigal Son Amongst the Swine), and gilt-bronze mounts.
Movement: Signed below the clock-face: *I. THURET . PARIS.*, also on back of movement. The movement is period and in working condition.

Dimensions: H. 57.2×34×15

This unusual clock is of the kind known as a *"Religieuse"* – housed in a portal-like case – which was produced in France in the earlier part of the reign of Louis XIV, in the first upsurge of clock-making that followed Huygens's invention of a new form of pendulum regulator, which he formally presented to the young King on 16th June, 1657.

But although the clock is French in form and has a French movement by Isaac Thuret (Clockmaker to the Observatory and to Louis XIV from 1684 until his death in 1706)[1], it is of a kind and quality apparently unique amongst French clocks of the period. Instead of the simple knopped feet, boulle-work veneer, and parapetted pavilion roof usually found in such clocks by Thuret and his contemporaries, it has gilt-bronze lions' feet, and jasper pilasters and inlays, including a pictorial scene of The Prodigal Son (acting as an admonition to the fruitful and virtuous use of time) in a pediment at the top. This *pietra dura* plaque is very close in style to a series of panels in the Museo dell'Opificio delle Pietre Dure in Florence. Most of these works date from the early years of the XVIIth century and can be connected with the designs of artists like Bernardino Poccetti, Ludovico Cigoli and Giovanni Bilivert; one of them showing Abraham entertaining the Angels, is slightly later and is now documented as made in 1620 by Giuliano Pandolfini. It is certain that most of them were made for the *ciborium* of the Cappella dei Principi in San Lorenzo, which was never set up in that church but was one of the great attractions in the Uffizi till the Grand Duke Pietro Leopoldo dismantled it. These early works of the Galleria show a distinct affinity to the work done in Prague for the Emperor Rudolf II by the Florentine *commettitori di pietre dura*, the Castrucci[3]. However, the panel inserted at the top of this clock appears closer in style to the ones made in the Grand-ducal Workshops and it displays slightly the naïve character of some of these early examples. Some other not very well known panels can be connected with all this early production: two landscapes in the Grünes Gewölbe in Dresden (inv. no. II. 71 and 72, 24×19 cm); Christ praying at the Mount of Olives (in the Museo del Prado 24.5×33.5 cm); St. Francis praying in a landscape

(formerly on the Milan art market); Christ and the Samaritan Woman at the well (Turin, 26.5 × 36.5 cm); St. Charles Borromeo writing: two versions of this plaque exist, one in the Hermitage and one in the Naturhistorisches Museum in Vienna[3]. It was by no means an unusual practice in the Louis XIV period to enhance pieces of furniture like this clock with *pietra dura* plaques. This is one of the reasons why a number of Florentine artisans were called to France and installed at the Gobelins. What is unusual however is to find in a piece of that period a panel of much earlier date.

1. Tardy, *Dictionnaire des Horlogers Français,* Paris, 1972, Vol. II, p. 614. According to Tardy, Thuret was active in the Galeries du Louvre in 1686.
2. Tardy, *La Pendule Française*, Paris, 1967, Vol. I, p. 97.
3. See the various entries on pp. 289-291 (by Anna Maria Giusti) on the catalogue *Il Museo dell'Opificio delle Pietre Dure a Firenze*, Milan, 1978. The Castrucci production in Prague has been studied by E. Neumann, "Florentiner Mosaik aus Prag", *Jahrbuch der Kunsthistorischen Kunstsammlungen in Wien*, 1957, 53, pp. 157-202.
   The panel in the Hermitage is illustrated in E. Efimova's *West European Mosaic of the 13th–19th centuries in the collection of the Hermitage*, Leningrad, 1963, fig. 5; the one in Turin in the catalogue by L. Mallé, *Vetri, vetrate, giade, cristalli di rocca e pietre dure*, Turin, 1971, p. 381, fig. 15.

A. G.-P.

GLASS, ROCK CRYSTAL

51 VENETIAN BEAKER.
Late XVth century.

Slightly convex-sided cylindrical beaker of almost colourless transparent glass (*cristallo*), with mould-blown raised ribs, the base pushed up in a low "kick", and the edge of the foot ornamented with an applied cordon of glass notched with the *pucellas* (tongs). The beaker is decorated with a deep border of leaf-gold which has been etched with a point into horizontal lines above and a fringe of square lappets below, while the main central zone bears a series of tangent ovals picked out in dots of white enamel grouped round a central red dot. The upper and lower horizontal lines are edged with blue dots, and the whole border is edged with a line of white dots below. The raised ribs are gilt.

Dimensions: H. 10.7 cm; Diam. of rim 7.5 cm

Beakers of this kind are rarer in Western collections than the goblets of the same technique which have bowls of very much this form mounted on a ribbed pedestal stem. The beakers, or fragments of them, however, do occur in excavations, and a group of three has been dug up in Southampton in a generally late-XVth century context. They are the counterparts of similar gilt and enamelled beakers excavated in the Near East; these last, however, nearly always have the ribs pinched sideways into a mesh design usually referred to as "nipt diamond waies" ("NDW"). It would seem from this evidence that the Venetian glassmakers catered specially for the tastes of their customers in their different overseas markets. The dotted ovals of the border on this piece, the serrated lower border, and the groups of three dots are characteristic of the Venetian enamelled and gilt glasses of this era.

A closely comparable beaker is in the Museum of Applied Arts in Prague, coming from the Lanna collection[1]. An example of more spreading form, and with the characteristic additional decoration of a blue thread encircling the glass above the ribbing, is in the Museo Civico, Turin[2]. Enamelled and gilt glasses are very seldom represented in contemporary Italian paintings, but a plain beaker almost identical in shape to the present example is shown in *The Nativity* of about 1475 by Hugo van der Goes, in the Galleria degli Uffizi, Florence ("The Portinari Altarpiece").

1. Exhibition of Venetian Glass, *Catalogue*, Prague, 1973, no. 9, fig. 7.
2. G. Mariacher, *Italian Blown Glass*, London, 1961, pl. 29.

General Bibliography:
R. Schmidt, "Die Venezianischen Emailglaser des XV. und XVI. Jahrhunderts", *Jahrbuch der Königlich Preuszischen Kunstsammlungen*, XXXII, 1911, pp. 249–86.
R. Schmidt, *Das Glas*, Berlin and Leipzig, 1922, pp. 89–99.
Corning Museum of Glass, *Three Great Centuries of Venetian Glass*, Corning, N.Y., 1958, pp. 27–61.
A. Gasparetto, *Il Vetro di Murano*, Venice, 1958, pp. 74 ff.
R. J. Charleston, "The Import of European Glass into the Near East", *Annales du 3e. Congrès des "Journées Internationales du Verre"*. Liège, 1965, pp. 158–168.

R. J. C.

52 VENETIAN BOWL.
Probably first half of XVIth century.

Bucket-shaped bowl (*secchiello*, probably a holy water aspersory) of colourless transparent glass (*cristallo*), decorated with vertical applied thread-decoration in opaque-white (*lattimo*) glass partially marvered in. These ornamental cordons are of plain ribbons ("a fil") and twisted multiple strands ("a ritortoli") alternately. The "bucket" has an overarching bail-handle which pivots in two plain side loops on the rim. The handle is itself decorated with spirals of *lattimo* thread marvered into its surface.

Dimensions: H. with handle raised 18 cm; Diam. of rim 14.3 cm

Glass holy water containers of this type are not particularly rare. Their use has been made clear in a picture dated 1495 by Vittore Carpaccio, showing *The Dream of St. Ursula* (Gallerie dell'Accademia, Venice). Beside the Saint's bed is a small shrine illuminated by a candle, and below it hangs a (metal) bucket of the same shape as the glass examples, with the handle of a sprinkler projecting from it. An example is known with enamelling of a type securely associated with Barcelona, and Spanish records make it clear that such "*calderitas*" were to be found in some numbers in noble households. Queen Isabel in 1503 had at least half-a-dozen, one described as of "clear glass, with a twisted handle of blue glass, resembling a bucket". Before 1560 the third Duke of Albuquerque had imported from Venice an example in engraved glass with a gilt handle and prunts, and a specimen answering to this description is in the British Museum[1]. Philip II had twenty-one Venetian glasses of this form in various sizes[2].

In an inventory (Harleian Ms. 1419) made in 1547 of the effects left by Henry VIII, "The Glasse House" contained, among some 600 Venetian glasses, "Itm a hollywater stoppe (i.e. stoup) of glasse with a baille (=bail, perhaps referring to the handle)". The last word, however, may read "laille" (=ladle), referring to the sprinkler. The stoup is not further described, but the inventory includes a number of items which are evidently decorated by the use of *lattimo* threads (e.g. "a bason and twoo lavers (ewers) of glasse all of diaper worke"; "xii bolles of glasse with one cover to theyme all wrought with Diap (diaper) worke white"). A number of these buckets in *lattimo*-striped glass are recorded[3]. They are variously dated. A number of examples in "ice-glass" must belong to the second half of the XVIth century, for this technique seems to be a relatively late one, the earliest reference (somewhat vague) dating from 1537. The earliest reference from Venice itself is significant. In 1570 an inventory of the glassmaker Bortolo d'Alvise, at the glasshouse of the "Three Moors", mentions "a bucket *a giazo*" (=ghiaccio=ice). It is clear that the shape lived on even into the XVIIIth century, an example occurring in the Danish Royal Collections at Rosenborg[4]. The Venetian items at Rosenborg were probably brought there in 1709.

Not all these buckets were necessarily used for holy water, however. A metal example is shown as an accessory of the banquet in Veronese's "Il Convito in Casa di Levi", dated 1573 (Gallerie dell'Accademia, Venice).

The present example, with its rather primitive decoration, the applied threads standing proud of the surface instead of being marvered in, probably dates from the first half of the XVIth century. (See no. 53.)

1. British Museum Exhibition, *The Golden Age of Venetian Glass, Catalogue* (by Hugh Tait), London, 1979, no. 227.
2. A. W. Frothingham, *Barcelona Glass in Venetian Style*, New York, 1956, p. 31, figs. 26–28.
3. e.g. Frothingham, *op. cit.*, fig. 27, in the Museos de Arte, Barcelona; Gasparetto, *op. cit.* below, fig. 69, Museo Vetrario, Murano; A. Ohm, *Europäisches und Aussereuropäisches Glas,* Frankfurt-am-Main, 1973, no. 161, in the Museum für Kunsthandwerk, Frankfurt.
4. G. Boesen, *Venetianske Glas på Rosenberg,* Copenhagen, 1960, no. 5.

General Bibliography:
R. Schmidt, *Das Glas,* Berlin and Leipzig, 1922, pp. 102 ff.
A. Gasparetto, *Il Vetro di Murano,* Venice, 1958, pp. 90 ff.
Corning Museum of Glass, *Three Great Centuries of Venetian Glass,* Corning, N.Y., 1958, pp. 69 ff.
L. Zecchin, "Fortuna d'una parola sbagliata", *Journal of Glass Studies,* X, 1968, pp. 110–113.
A. Polak, "Venetian Renaissance Glass: the problems of dating *vetro a filigrana*", *The Connoisseur,* August, 1976, pp. 270–277.
British Museum Exhibition, *The Golden Age of Venetian Glass, Catalogue* (by Hugh Tait), London, 1979, pp. 49 ff.

R. J. C.

53 VENETIAN GOBLET.
Middle or second half of XVIth century.

Goblet of greyish *cristallo*, with bell-shaped bowl, the lower part of which is decorated with a diaper of projecting mould-blown bosses. The stem is composed of a depressed spherical knop between mereses (discs) and is set on a plain pedestal foot with folded edge. The whole glass is decorated "a retortoli" with multi-ply cables of opaque-white glass (*lattimo*) partially marvered into the crystal base-glass. A diagonal effect has been imparted to these during the working of the glass.

Dimensions: H. 15 cm; Diam. of rim 10 cm

The decoration of glass by the use of bands and twists incorporating opaque-white glass probably dates to the early years of the XVIth century, and may even have been used in exceptional cases before 1500. In 1527 two brothers, Filippo and Bernardino Catanei, working at the glasshouse with the sign of the Syren (Sirena), applied for a twenty-five year patent for making glass by

a new technique of their invention "a facete con retortoli a fil" ("in stripes with twists of thread"). Their privilege was granted for a term of ten years on 19th October, 1527. Vannoccio Biringuccio in his treatise *De la Pirotechnia* (Venice, 1540) alludes to "the drinking vessels in which one actually sees twisted designs of thorn branches and other criss-cross inlays. Look, too, at the large things, as well as the small, that they make of white or coloured glass and that seem to be woven of osier twigs equally spaced with the greatest uniformity and exactness of termination". This last phrase perhaps referred to the way in which the vertical stripes were pinched together at the base of the vessel and the surplus then neatly snipped off leaving the impression that all radiated from a single point. When the paraison (bubble of inflation) had been finished in this way, it could be worked like a plain glass, even being blown, as in the present case, into a mould to form the lower part of the bowl.

Glasses of this particular form are relatively numerous[1]. To the examples cited, there may be added one with sparse stripes "a fil" in the British Museum[2]; another with more closely spaced stripes "a fil" in the Corning Museum[3]; an apparently excavated example with stripes "a fil" and "a retortoli" in the Grosvenor Museum and Art Gallery, Chester[4].

There are very few clues to the dating of these glasses. One example, in the Baar Collection in the Museum at Liège, has been broken and mounted as a stirrup cup with a silver mount having a bell-finial. This is engraved with the arms of Sarah Vincx (d. 1647), who in 1584 married Ambrosio Mongarda, a master glassmaker of Antwerp[5]. The glass may have been old at this date, however, and in general these glasses conform with the low proportions of the glasses made in the first half of the XVIth century, with central knop and pedestal foot, rather than baluster stem and disc-foot. Their relatively complex decoration, however, suggests a date about the middle of the XVIth century or slightly later.

1. Charleston, *op. cit.* below, pp. 165, n. 7; Polak, *op. cit.,* p. 275.
2. *The Golden Age of Venetian Glass, op. cit.,* no. 155.
3. *Three Great Centuries, op. cit.,* no. 67.
4. Merseyside County Museums, *Historic Glass,* Liverpool, 1979, no. D6; etc.
5. R. Chambon, *L'Histoire de la Verrerie en Belgique,* Brussels, 1955, p. 315, pl. XIV, 49.

General Bibliography:
R. Schmidt, *Das Glas,* Berlin and Leipzig, pp. 67–75, 102 ff.
A. Gasparetto, *Il Vetro di Murano,* Venice, 1958, pp. 90 ff.
Corning Museum of Glass, *Three Great Centuries of Venetian Glass,* Corning, N.Y., (1958), pp. 69 ff.
L. Zecchin, "Famiglie Vetrarie Famose: I Serena", *Vetro e Silicate,* Anno VIII, N. 44, March-April, 1964, pp. 17–20.
Id. "Una fornace muranese all'insegna della Sirena", *Rivista della Stazione Sperimentale del Vetro,* Murano, no 2, 1971.
R. J. Charleston, "Glass in the Gambier-Parry Collection", *The Burlington Magazine,* March, 1967, pp. 165.
A. Polak, "Venetian Renaissance Glass", *op. cit.,* pp. 270–77

R. J. C.

54 VENETIAN JAR.
Second half of XVIth century.

Jar, transparent colourless glass (*cristallo*) decorated with canes of opaque-white (*lattimo*) glass. Bands of cable-pattern ("a retortoli") abut each other to cover the whole surface. The glass has been blown into a mould to produce a relief-pattern of lions facing a spreadeagle, with gadrooning above and below. The spreading lip has been folded outwards, and the base is formed by an applied cordon of plain glass. The relief portions of the decoration shows traces of gilding.

Dimensions: H. 9.2 cm; Diam. of rim 6 cm

The technical background of these *lattimo*-threaded glasses has already been sketched under a previous item (see no. 53).

A number of pieces of XVIth and XVIIth century glass have been blown in three or four-part moulds, imparting to the vessel a fixed form and decoration which the glassmaker did his best to retain unaltered. Of these designs there are two versions which employ the theme of lions, somewhat ineptly rendered. One shows between pairs of lions a shield of arms[1], the other has two lions and two double-headed spreadeagles, as in the present case[2], a vase in the Victoria and Albert Museum, and a flask formerly in the Walter F. Smith Collection, Trenton, N.J.[3]. The double-headed eagle, but between plant scrolls, recurs on a ewer in the Liège Museum[4].

The late R. Chambon argued on the basis of a goblet mould-blown with the arms of the City and Marquisate of Antwerp that these fixed-mould pieces were probably made at Antwerp, the centre of an important manufacture "à la façon de Venise"[5]. An inventory taken in 1578 of a Murano glasshouse, however, included "una forma de fiaschi a meduse" ("a mould for bottles with Medusa heads"). Since glasses mould-blown with this theme of decoration exist, it is reasonable to suppose that they are of Venetian origin, and that other comparable mould-blown designs were used there[6].

Since the design on the present piece is bounded above and below by gadrooning, it seems probable that the mould was intended primarily for vases, flasks and jugs. The present shape seems not to be recorded. Such moulds were, however, occasionally used for apparently unsuitable shapes (e.g. a handled bucket with criss-cross white-threaded decoration "a reticella" formerly in the Melvin Billups Collection, New York[7]).

1. British Museum, *The Golden Age of Venetian Glass, op. cit.,* no. 156; Liège, *Trois Millénaires d'Art Verrier,* 1958, no. 495; Corning, *Three Great Centuries of Venetian Glass, op. cit.,* no. 69.
2. *The Golden Age of Venetian Glass, op. cit.,* no. 157; ill. *Journal of Glass Studies,* IV, 1962, pp. 144, no. 27.
3. *Journal of Glass Studies,* IV, (1962), p. 144, no. 27.
4. *Trois Millénaires d'Art Verrier, op. cit.,* no. 275.
5. "Verres de la Renaissance soufflés dans un moule fermé", *Glastechnische Berichte,* Bd. 32 K, Heft VIII, 1959, pp. 49–56.
6. L. Zecchin, "Una fornace Muranese all'Insegna dell'Angelo", *Vetro e Silicati,* XI, no. 62, 1967, p. 26.
7. Corning Museum of Glass, *A Decade of Glass Collecting,* Corning, N.Y., 1962, no. 41.

General Bibliography:
R. Schmidt, *Das Glas,* Berlin and Leipzig, 1922, pp. 102 ff.
A. Gasparetto, *Il Vetro di Murano,* Venice, 1958, pp. 90 ff.
Corning Museum of Glass, *Three Great Centuries of Venetian Glass,* Corning, N.Y., 1958, pp. 69 ff., especially nos. 67–9.
R. J. Charleston, "Glass" in *The James A. de Rothschild Collection at Waddesdon Manor, Glass and Enamels,* Fribourg, 1977, pp. 124–6.

R. J. C.

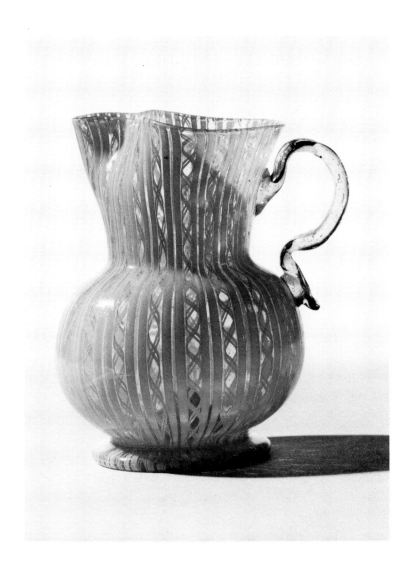

55 VENETIAN JUG.
Probably second half of XVIth century.

Jug of clear colourless glass (*cristallo*) decorated with stripes of opaque-white (*lattimo*) glass. Two plain bands (*a fil*) alternate with one of cable-pattern (*a retortoli*). The low foot is made in one piece with the body. The undecorated handle is joined to the body at the lower point of attachment by a small pad of plain glass.

Dimensions: H. 11.5 cm; Diam. of body 8.5 cm

The technical background to this type of glass has been discussed under a previous item (see no. 53). Jugs decorated in this manner, however, are far from common, and no exact parallel to this jug has been found, perhaps because on the whole pottery or metal jugs were used in conjunction with drinking glasses, as may be seen from various contemporary *genre* paintings. A number of glass jugs of technically distinctive XVIIth century types, however, survive and seem to demonstrate a strong tendency for the body to widen at the shoulders and for the lip to assume a pronounced broad trefoil shape[1]. The present jug, however, seems only a slight modification of the XVIth century tankard with globular body and cylindrical neck[2].

1. e.g. Corning, *Three Great Centuries of Venetian Glass, op. cit.,* nos. 98, 99, 122.
2. e.g. British Museum, *The Golden Age of Venetian Glass, op. cit.,* no. 81.

General Bibliography:
H. Schmidt, *Das Glas,* Berlin and Leipzig, 1922, pp. 102 ff.
A. Gasparetto, *Il Vetro di Murano,* Venice, 1958, pp. 90 ff.
Corning Museum of Glass, *Three Great Centuries of Venetian Glass,* Corning, N.Y., pp. 69 ff.
A. Polak, "Venetian Renaissance Glass: the problems of dating *vetro a filigrana*", *The Connoisseur,* August, 1976, pp. 270–77.

R. J. C.

56   VENETIAN (?) "GOBLET VASE"
Second half of XVIth century or early XVIIth century.

"Goblet vase", greyish-colourless transparent glass (*cristallo*), the surface treated by the "ice-glass" technique, probably by plunging the bowl, while hot, into cold water. Prior to this the paraison was blown into a vertically ribbed mould, as were subsequently the components of the stem and foot. To these embellishments were added horizontal applied borders, the top two composed of a blue-and-white cable between white threads, the lowest by white threads only. Below this the base of the bowl is gilt, as are parts of the stem and foot. The stem is elaborately compiled of six elements, most vertically ribbed and gilt. The foot is decorated with radiating ribbing.

Dimensions: H. 21 cm; Diam. of rim 10.4 cm

Glasses of this general form were made in different parts of Europe. "Goblet vases", recognisable by idiosyncrasies of decoration, may confidently be attributed, for example, to Spain[1]; or to the glasshouses at Innsbruck, in Austria[2]. They were certainly also made in the Southern Netherlands, for the *Catalogue* of the Beauwelz glasshouse, datable to about 1550–55, illustrates a

glass of this character, accompanied by the caption, "Verres cibores a panse pour vin ou bier en verre craquelé ou non." ("Bellied Ciborium glasses for wine or beer in crackled glass or plain.") That such glasses were in fact used for liturgical purposes seems to be demonstrated by a picture showing such a glass in an ecclesiastical setting. The painting is by Francesco Pacheco (1654–1654) of Seville, and is dated 1611 (Bowes Museum, Barnard Castle). Equally certainly they were used for secular purposes, presumably for drinking wine and beer, as the Beauwelz *Catalogue* demonstrates; but probably also for flowers. Examples are depicted in still-life paintings by Willem Kalf, 1619–93, one in the Boymans Museum, Rotterdam, the other in the Springfield Museum of Fine Arts, U.S.A.[3]. In both pictures the goblet vase – no doubt the same vessel – is shown as of "ice-glass" with applied prunts and hollow-blown stem of the "lion mask" type. Very similar glasses are in the Corning Museum itself (from the Jerome Strauss Collection) and in the Victoria and Albert Museum, London[4]: they are reasonably attributed to a Netherlands glasshouse. These glasses have round-based bowls, but the slightly pointed bowl of the present glass is also commonly found, and of two matching goblet-vases in Vienna one has the round-base and the other the ovoid. Both are of "ice-glass" with the mixed blue-and-white cable decoration of the present example, and both come from Schloss Ambras, in the Tyrol, whither thay are thought to have been sent from Venice in 1568[5]. They seem to demonstrate the interchangeable character of these two main forms. The British Museum possesses the counterpart round-based model of the glass under discussion, for the stem-formation is virtually identical although the thread-circuits are in opaque-white only and are punctuated with gilt prunts[6].

The "ice-glass" technique appears to have been a relative latecomer in the Venetian repertory. The earliest reference comes from Spain, the poet Gracilaso de la Vega listing in 1537 thirty-two pieces of Venetian glass, some "frosted", which suggests the effect: the same expression is used of Venetian glasses belonging to Philip II in the Prado in 1564[7]. The first reference in Venice itself, however, dates only from 1570, when the glassmaker Bortolo d'Alvise had a bucket "a giazo" (=*ghiaccio*=ice) in his inventory[8].

1. E. Schrijver, *Glass and Crystal,* London, 1963, pl. 17a.
2. Erich Egg, *Die Glashütten zu Hall und Innsbruck im XVI Jahrhundert*, Innsbruck, 1962, figs. 27–35.
3. Corning Museum of Glass, *Glass Vessels in Dutch Painting of the 17th century*, 1952, pl. VII.
4. W. B. Honey, *Glass: a Handbook*, London, 1946, p. 64, pl. 31, c.
5. E. Egg, *op. cit.*, p. 44, figs. 25–6.
6. *The Golden Age of Venetian Glass, op. cit.*, no. 151.
7. A. W. Frothingham, *Barcelona Glass in Venetian Style,* New York, 1956, pp. 16, 19.
8. L. Zecchin, "Bortolo d'Alvisi ai Tre Mori", *Velio e silicati anno XIII,* no. 76, (1969), p. 4.

General Bibliography:
A. Gasparetto, *Il Vetro di Murano,* Venice, 1958, p. 92.
R. Schmidt, *Das Glas,* Berlin and Leipzig, 1922, pp. 110–111, 129.
R. Chambon, *Histoire de la Verrerie en Belgique,* Brussels, 1955, pp. 103 ff., 312, nos. 27–29.
R. J. Charleston, "Glass" in *The James A. de Rothschild Collection at Waddesdon Manor, Glass and Enamels*, 1977, pp. 112–115.

R. J. C.

57 VENETIAN GOBLET.
    First half of XVIIth century.

Goblet of greyish-colourless transparent glass (*cristallo*). The exaggerated thistle-shaped bowl is mounted on a tall hollow-blown stem composed of a short upper baluster separated by a depressed spherical element from a taller slender inverted baluster, all made in one piece. This stem is joined to the bowl and foot by mereses (solid discs), the lower of which has been worked up over the bottom of the hollow-blown stem.

    Dimensions: H. 19.5 cm; Diam. of rim 11.2 cm

This goblet belongs to the classic repertory of three-piece glasses (bowl, tall stem, disc foot) which evolved in Venice during the second half of the XVIth century and continued into the XVIIth.

    A goblet with thistle bowl but more elaborate stem is shown in the painting of *The Prodigal Son* by Gerard van Honthorst (1592–1660), in the Alte Pinakothek in Munich; and a glass with slightly less exaggerated thistle-bowl but with a tall hollow-blown stem comparable to the present example appears in a still-life painting by Simon Luttichuys (1610–c. 1662) shown in the International Art Treasures Exhibition, Bath, in 1973. A goblet with an exaggeratedly long thistle bowl is shown in a still-life dated 1632 by Willem-Claes Heda (1594–1678), exhibited in the Antique Dealers' Fair, London, in 1968. Here, however, the bowl is decorated with ear-shaped handles in coloured glass.

    A number of parallels may be cited. In the British Museum is a goblet 21.5 cm high with a longer bowl than the present example, mounted on a hollow stem of diminishing knops[1], while an even taller (26.8 cm) glass in the Merseyside County Museums has an equally long bowl on a single hollow inverted baluster of slender proportions[2]. A 19 cm glass in the Krug Collection has the long bowl, slightly less exaggerated in profile, on a considerably shorter inverted baluster stem[3], and two surviving glasses show the thistle bowl mounted on a plain tapering conical stem, all these being hollow-blown (Osterreichisches Museum für Angewandte Kunst, Vienna)[4].

The simpler form of these last two glasses suggests for them a date in the latter part of the XVIth century. A plain glass with bell-shaped bowl is indeed shown in the illustrated catalogue of the Beauwelz glasshouse (modern Belgium) dating from about 1550–55[5].

1.   *The Golden Age of Venetian Glass, op. cit.,* no. 48.
2.   *Historic Glass, op. cit.,* no. D 11.
3.   B. Klesse, *Glassammlung Helfried Krug,* II, Bonn, 1973, no. 480.
4.   I. Schlosser, *Venezianer Gläser,* Vienna, 1951, pl. 12, 17.5 cm high.
5.   R. Chambon, *L'Histoire de la Verrerie en Belgique* Brussels, 1955, pl. P, a.

General Bibliography:
R. Schmidt, *Das Glas,* Berlin and Leipzig, 1922, pp. 67 ff.
Victoria and Albert Museum, *Glass: a Handbook* . . . (by W. B. Honey), London, 1946, pp. 56 ff.
J. Schlosser, *Venezianer Gläser,* Vienna, 1951, pp. 3 ff.

R. J. C.

Perhaps Florence or Pisa, XVIIth century.

Pair of vases, blue glass with faint vertical mould-blown ribbing, mounted in gilt base metal. The vessels have been pinched in at the middle to give a boat-shape, and below the foot a button of glass has been contrived to provide anchorage for the mount, which consists of openwork straps terminating in dragonesque forms and joining a horizontal fillet of square chain-design above with a calyx of fleur-de-lys surmounting the turned foot with mouldings below.

Dimensions: H. to top of handles 14 cm and 13.5 cm;
L. of bowls 16.5 cm and 15.5 cm

The centre which made these coloured purely ornamental glasses is as yet not identified. The rather thick material (emerald-green and blue-green also occur) seems uncharacteristic of Venetian glass, and very few colourless (*cristallo*) glasses are mounted in this style, which is fairly consistent for the whole group of coloured examples. A design for a glass of the shape of the present pair, shown in a metal mount with some of the same features, is in the public collections in Florence, and is attributed to Jacopo Ligozzi (c. 1547–1626), who executed a whole series of more or less fanciful designs for glass, presumably intended for execution – as far as this was possible – in the Grand Ducal Glasshouse. From 1579 a furnace under the Venetian master Bortolo from the glasshouse of "The Three Moors" at Murano was working in the Medici Gardens between S. Marco and Via S. Gallo, and remained through the reigns of Francesco I and Ferdinando I (d. 1609). In 1618 Cosimo II had a furnace built in the gardens of the Pitti Palace, put under the direction of another Venetian, Jacomo della Luna. Other furnaces opened later in the century. The Grand Ducal furnaces were established more to give pleasure to their patrons in the execution of complicated commissions than to compete in the open market, and a number of drawings by Stefano della Bella and Jacques Callot, apart from Ligozzi, testify to the fantastical character of the Florentine glasses. A possible argument for a Florentine origin for these glasses is the constant recurrence in the mounts of the fleur-de-lys, the emblem of Florence (the *giglio*).

Another possible source of origin of these coloured glasses is Pisa, where Cosimo I had founded a glasshouse, and where the priest Antonio Neri, the father of glass technology, is known to have conducted a number of experiments in the making of coloured glasses in 1602. A third possibility is Naples, where glass is known to have been made in both the XVIth and the XVIIIth centuries. Glasses of this character occasionally occur in the painting of artists connected with either Naples or Madrid, Naples at this time being a part of the dominions of Spain.

Closely similar pieces are in the Victoria and Albert Museum, London (Mus. no. 19–1867) and the James A. de Rothschild Collection at Waddesdon Manor[1].

1.   R. J. Charleston, "Glass" in *The James A. de Rothschild Collection at Waddesdon Manor: Glass and Enamels*, Fribourg, 1977, pp. 21–5, 128–142.

59 SPANISH WINE GLASS.
(Probably Barcelona), Mid or late XVIth century.

Tall-stemmed three-piece wine glass, of lightly bubbled greenish transparent glass, with vertical stripes of opaque-white applied to the bowl and marvered in. Hollow-blown tapering stem and disc-foot.

Dimensions: H. 14.5 cm; Diam. of rim 11 cm

The shape and the colour of this glass betray its Spanish origin. A further pointer in the same direction is the technique of applying the opaque-white decoration. The stripes do not in all cases reach the centre of the base of the bowl, whereas in Venetian practice the canes were pinched together to a single point and the surplus cut away (see no. 53). The glass admirably represents the *façon de Venise* transplanted to Spanish soil, and there were writers in the XVIth and XVIIth centuries who claimed that Catalan glass surpassed the Venetian: "The glass that today is made in Venice is considered excellent . . . but . . . in many ways, that made in Barcelona and other parts of Cataluña is better . . . (Pere Gil, a late XVIth century Catalan priest, *cit.* Frothingham, *op. cit.*, p. 30). The industry had been centred in Barcelona since at latest the XVth century, and became famous towards the end of it. The Venetian *lattimo*-striped glass was called in Spain "lo rayado a la manera de Venecia" ("striped glass in the Venetian manner").

A closely similar glass is in the Corning Museum of Glass, N.Y.[1] and a slightly coarser and probably later example is in the same Museum[2].

1. R. J. Charleston, *Masterpieces of Glass,* New York, 1980, pp. 104–5.
2. A. W. Frothingham, *Spanish Glass,* London, 1964, pl. 29.

R. J. C.

60 GLASS WITH PUTTI.
Probably the Netherlands, third quarter of XVIIth century.

Goblet of greenish-colourless glass, wheel-engraved. The pointed round-funnel bowl is mounted on a hollow-blown stem composed of a flattened ribbed knop above and a plain inverted baluster below, separated from each other and from the bowl and foot by means of mereses and a reel-shaped element, all of plain glass. The plain disc-foot has a thin edge-fold. The bowl is superficially wheel-engraved with a *putto* holding a cornucopia from which issues a vine-trail. To either side are other *putti*, one holding a bow and arrow, the second corn-stalks. At the back is a sunburst, its centre carefully polished. Below the figures is a plant-scroll border with sparse leaves and berries; and round the foot a wreath of leaves.

Dimensions: H. 19 cm; Diam. of rim 9.5 cm

It is uncertain where this glass was made. The very superficial style of the engraving, however, seems to affiliate it to a number of examples which appear to be at home in the Netherlands. That glass was being wheel-engraved there by about the middle of the XVIIth century appears from one or two dated or otherwise documentary glasses which betray their Netherlands origin by their shape. The earliest of these is probably a goblet in the Dordrecht Museum commemorating a Dutch naval victory over the Swedes, dated 1659. In the Toledo Museum, Ohio, U.S.A., is a green *Roemer* of a type universally found in Holland, engraved with grotesques after Callot by an artist signing himself Carel du Quesne, and dated 1661. A goblet in the Musées Royaux d'Art et d'Histoire, Brussels[1], engraved with *putti* amidst vine-scrolls, is dated 1663. A group of glasses with comparably superficial engraving have idiosyncratic openwork stems terminating in parrot-like beaked heads. Two are in the Brussels Museum, one with a Netherlands marriage coat-of-arms supported by *putti*, the other with *putti* engaged in the grape harvest[2]. Both glasses have a polished "printie" on the reverse, corresponding to the centre of the sunburst on the glass under discussion. This common device enabled the spectator to view the remaining engraved decoration as through a lens. These sunbursts recur on two further glasses with the "parrot's head" stems[3] and the "printie" alone on a Dutch-inscribed glass of typical Netherlands shape in the Gemeente Museum, The Hague[4]. All these are decorated with figural subjects, usually on a fairly large scale, rendered in shallow engraving unpolished except for the sunbursts; and the predominance of *putti* amidst vines may be noted. This subject matter recurs on a green *Roemer* in the Boymans Museum, Rotterdam[5]. A goblet in the Liège Museum is wheel-engraved with a representation of Queen Christina of Sweden on horseback, with the arms of Philip IV (1621–65) of Spain on one side, and those of Antwerp on the other.

After her abdication Christina arrived in Antwerp in 1654, and stayed there for two years, and it may be supposed that the glass was engraved not very long after this event. The stem of the glass is composed of two quatrefoil knops, a form common in the Netherlands in the period about 1670–90, and there seems every likelihood that the goblet was made in one of the Bonhommes' glasshouses in Antwerp[6]. The same may well be true of the remainder of the group.

1. A. M. Berryer, *La Verrerie Ancienne*, Brussels, 1957, pl. XXXII, b.
2. See Note 1, pl. XL, a and b.
3. E. Schenk zu Schweinsberg, "Einige Belgische Gläser aus dem XVII en Jahrhundert", *Paper* 257, read to the Brussels Conference of the International Congress on Glass, 1965, figs. B and C.
4. B. Jansen, *Catalogus van Noord – en Zuidnederlands glas*, The Hague, 1962, no. 134.
5. C. Isings, *Schönes altes Glas,* Hanover, 1966, pl. 77.
6. R. Chambon, *op. cit.,* p. 321, pl. XXVII, 83.

R. J. C.

61 GERMAN BEAKER.
Probably Upper Franconia (Fichtelgebirge region): dated 1615.

Cylindrical beaker (*Humpen*) of slightly brownish glass, the base pushed up in a low conical "kick", the footrim formed of an overlapping coil of glass. Painted in enamel colours with some use of gold. Painted in the front with the crowned and nimbed spreadeagle symbolising the Holy Roman Empire, with the arms of its component parts displayed on the wings, and the orb of sovereignty on the breast. Inscribed: "Das heilige römisch (*sic*) reich mitt sampt seinnen (sic) gliedernn 1615" ("The Holy Roman Empire with all its components 1615"). Above is a border consisting of diagonal lines of blue, red and green dots on a gold ground, this border edged below by a double line of white dots and above by a white cable motif, the whole surmounted by a border of intersecting arcs forming a cresting with fernlike finials all in white. Above the foot runs a cable border between plain lines, above a fillet of alternating lenticular and lozenge motifs formed by intersecting arcs, all in white. The footrim is painted with radiating white dashes.

Dimensions: H. 20.5 cm; Diam. of rim 10 cm

One of the most prolific areas for the production of enamelled glass in Germany was the region to the west of the heavily wooded Fichtelgebirge, which formed the frontier of Germany and Bohemia. Here Bischofsgrün and one or two smaller centres produced enamelled glasses, while Kreussen, not far away, made brown salt-glazed stoneware with comparable enamelling. In the XVIIth century Bischofsgrün boasted three glasshouses.

Of all the German enamelled glasses the great *Reichsadlerhumpen* ("Imperial Eagle *Humpen*") – were both the commonest and perhaps the most imposing. They commemorate an ideal rather than a real order, with the hierarchy of the Empire represented by the Electors at the top and by vertical rows of four shields, each representing a "Quaternion" or constituent part of the Empire (Dukes, Margraves, Burggraves, Freiherrn, etc.). This system was first published by Peter von Andlau in his *De Imperio Romano* (c. 1460), and the graphic sources showing the eagle and "Quaternions" go back almost as early. The version used on the *Humpen* is close to one published by Hans Burgkmair in 1510, but this showed a crucifix in place of the orb, which takes its place later in the XVIth century (in e.g. Jans Bussemaker's engraving of 1587).

These glasses were used for the most solemn toasts, and when not in use were stored out of harm's way on the cornice above the wainscot. A German writer of 1616 refers to "the great monstrous Humpen which is called the 'Römische Reich' . . . ." and prescribes that one should "wipe the dust off the 'Römische Reich' and other drinking-vessels" and "set on foot a jolly toping and tippling party". Some of these glasses held as much as five quarts.

A number of Franconian glasses show borders similar to those on this glass, e.g. a *Humpen* in the Victoria and Albert Museum, London[1].

1.   Axel von Saldern, *op. cit.,* fig. 66.

General Bibliography:
Axel von Saldern, *German Enamelled Glass*, Corning, N.Y., 1965, pp. 51–67, 182–196.
Robert Schmidt, *Das Glas,* Berlin and Leipzig, 1922, pp. 163–9, 185–194
T. Ostertag, *Das Fichtelsgebirgsglas*, Erlangen, 1933.
R. J. Charleston, "Glass" in *The James A. de Rothschild Collection at Waddesdon Manor: Glass and Enamels,* Fribourg, 1977, pp. 28–30.

R. J. C.

62 GERMAN BEAKER.
Hesse (probably glasshouse of Adam Götze "unter Münden" on the Olbe, dated 1660).

Cylindrical beaker (*Humpen*) of greenish glass, the base pushed up in a conical "kick", the footrim formed of an overlapping coil of glass. Painted in enamel colours (red, brown-black, yellow, white, yellowish-green and blue) with some use of gold. Painted in the front with the arms of Hesse[1], for the Landgraf Wilhelm VI of Hesse (d. 1663); and on the reverse with a version of the arms of Brandenburg, for the Landgräfin Hedwig Sophie, sister of Kurfürst Friedrich Wilhelm of Brandenburg ("The Great Elector"). Below the rim is a border consisting of alternating lenticular and lozenge motifs formed by intersecting arcs of white dots, on a gold band bordered above and below by double lines of white dots. The field on a gold band bordered above and below by double lines of white dots. The field surrounding the coat-of-arms is partially filled with gold lozenges enlivened by blue and red dots; white calligraphic flourishes; white rosettes; and a grating motif of crossing white lines. The footrim is painted with radiating white dashes.

Dimensions: H. 25 cm; Diam. of rim 11.5 cm

The localisation of German enamelled glasses is fraught with difficulties and uncertainties. The presence of a princely coat-of-arms, however, is *prima facie* evidence that the glass was made in that prince's dominions, probably for the Court Pantry ("Hofkellerei"). With the present glass the markedly green tint of the material is a further indication that it is indeed of Hessian origin.

On 21st January, 1657, Adam Götze obtained a concession to set up a glasshouse "unter Münden an der Olbe", the Olbe being a tributary of the River Weser. A list from Götze's glasshouse, dated 1658, includes "Gilt armorial glasses" ("Vergülte Wapenglase") at a price of one Thaler each.

1. *J. Siebmacher's grosses und allgemeines Wappenbuch* (ed. O. T. von Hefner), Nuremberg, 1856, I, pl. 59.

    General Bibliography:
    Robert Schmidt, *Das Glas,* Berlin and Leipzig, 1922, pp. 195–8.
    M. Killing, *Die Glasmacherkunst in Hessen,* Marburg, 1927, pp. 58 ff.
    Axel von Saldern, *German Enamelled Glass,* Corning, N.Y., 1965, pp. 214–218.
    F. A. Dreier, *Glaskunst in Hessen-Kassel,* Kassel, 1968.
    Gustav Weiss, *The Book of Glass,* London, 1971, p. 132.

R. J. C.

119

63 POTSDAM GOBLET.

c. 1710–1720.

Goblet of colourless glass, cut and engraved on the wheel. Round-funnel bowl on a stem composed of a solid knop above a solid inverted baluster, joined to each other and to bowl and foot by solid discs. All these elements, and the base of the bowl, are cut in relief (*Hochschnitt*) with acanthus-leaf motifs. Below the rim is a border of lozenges alternating with ovals, separated from each other by groups of one large and four small circular cuts. Below this is a line of tangent circles ("printies"). The body of the bowl is wheel-engraved with two *putti* dancing to a tune played on the *viola da gamba* by (?) Orpheus. On the reverse is a woman revealing a cupid with a bow, while with the other hand she holds a second cupid. Behind her is an old man in a long robe, and beside him a young man kneeling in a deferential posture.

Dimensions: H. 20.5 cm; Diam. of rim 10 cm

This is a characteristic glass made at the Elector of Brandenburg's glasshouse at Potsdam, founded in 1679. By the date of the glass under discussion, a fine "crystal" material was being made by the addition of lime to a potash-glass. Blown thick, it offered a wonderful vehicle for the wheel-engraver, and in its early days the glasshouse attracted talents of the highest order – notably Martin Winter, who had undoubtedly learned his craft in Silesia; and his nephew Gottfried Spiller, one of the greatest of all glass engravers. Martin was taken on in 1680 and Spiller in 1683. In 1688 a water-driven mill was installed, making it possible to execute work in high relief (*Hochschnitt*), which required a great expenditure of energy. Wheel-engraving was executed on an apparatus driven by a foot treadle, and the engraving workshop was in Berlin itself. Winter died in 1702, but Spiller was still alive in 1721. Spiller's superbly executed engraving, with soft modelling and brilliantly polished detail, was never equalled by the supporting team of glass-engravers who worked in the Berlin workshop, some of whose names are known from documents, but whose work remains unidentified. The present glass must be attributed to one of these secondary talents.

Comparable goblets are in the Märkisches Museum, East Berlin[1], in the Brauser Collection, Munich[2], and one formerly in the Neues Palais, Potsdam[3]. The present glass would originally have had a cover, its formal decoration (jewelled border, relief-acanthus, etc.) matching that of the goblet.

1.   Ekhart Berckenhagen, *Berliner und Märkische Gläser*, Darmstadt, 1956, pl. 15.
2.   W. Bernt, *Altes Glass,* Munich, (n.d. but 1951), pl. 78.
3.   R. Schmidt, *Brandenburghische Gläser,* Berlin, 1914, plate 21, c

R. J. C.

64   PERSIAN BOTTLE.
      Second half of XVIIth century.

Tapering bottle, alkaline-glazed pottery painted in brown lustre on a pale-blue glaze. Ibex and birds are shown among bristling trees, large-leaved plants and scattered flowers and leaves. At the bottom of the neck and above the base of the bottle are borders of intersecting leaf-like arabesques. The neck is decorated with feathery and large-leafed foliage.

        Dimensions: H. 30.5 cm; Diam. of lip 3.7 cm

After the medieval period, when Kashan was the main centre of manufacture of lustre-painted pottery, the technique hung on in rather debased forms until the XVth century, when it seems to have perished. It was revived, however, in the Safavid period with rendering of plants, flowers, trees and occasionally animals and birds, painted in lustre-pigments ranging in tone from brown to rich ruby-red, applied on white or occasionally (as here) tinted glazes. The shapes made were mostly small (bottles, vases, covered bowls, etc.), perhaps because the lustre-painting had to be fixed by a second firing in a reducing atmosphere contrived in a small secondary kiln. It is not known where in Persia these wares were made, but Shiraz is a possibility.
   Pieces comparable to the present example are in the Victoria and Albert Museum[1], the Godman Collection[2], Cincinatti Art Museum[3].

1.   A. Lane, *op. cit.* below, pl. 84A.
2.   Arts Council of Great Britain, *The Arts of Islam*, London, 1976, no. 402.
3.   Charles K. Wilkinson, *Iranian Ceramics*, New York, 1963, no. 95.

      General Bibliography:
      B. Rackham, *Islamic Pottery and Italian Maiolica*, London, 1959, p. 18.
      A. Lane, *Later Islamic Pottery*, London, 1957, pp. 102–4.
      O. Watson, "Persian Lustre Ware, from the 14th to the 19th century", *Le Monde Iranian et L'Islam*, III, Paris, 1975, pp. 63–80.

                                                                R. J. C.

65 THE RAPE OF HELEN.
Majolica, Francesco Xanto Avelli, Urbino, 1534.

Six Trojans in a boat, two of them trying to drag Helen on board; Greek warriors struggling to prevent her leaving and one of them holding her by her robe. In the middle distance Trojan boats are seen arriving with warriors disembarking. In the centre of the dish is a group of fighting soldiers; in the background an architectural fantasy. On the reverse: the date M.D.XXXIIII, some verses:

"Quest'é 'l pastor che mal miró 'l bel volto
D'Helena Greca, e, quel famoso rapto
pel qual fu 'l mondo sotto sopra volto"

and the signature: *Fza: Xàto. A.*
da Rovigo,
Urbino.

Diameter: 46 cm

The subject derives from an engraving by Marcantonio Raimondi after Raphael (Bartsch, XIV, 209). The scene is somewhat rearranged, and is typical of the artist's work.

L. d'U.

66   ROCK CRYSTAL EWER.
Workshop of Ottavio Miseroni, Milan, late XVIth century.

Formed as a galley with spout at each end, that at the front formed by a grotesque mask, the body carved with scrolling foliage and festoons of fruit centering on each side on a male term springing from a bunch of fruit on shaped plinth, baluster stem and oval foot, the stem and foot mounts of enamelled gold, the latter with an applied wreath of jewelled cartouche-shaped members.

Dimensions: H. 19 cm; W. 29 cm

The bowl, which was originally completed with a cover, dates from the late XVIth century, the stem, foot and mounts appear to be later. The arrangement of the ornament on this bowl with its festoons of fruit is typical of the Miseroni style in the closing years of the XVIth century. A comparable scheme can be seen on the body of the ewer[1] made for Duke Johann Friedrich von Württemberg in the Schatzkammer of the Munich residence. This vessel was completed before 1615. Two rock-crystal galleys of somewhat earlier date are also preserved in the Munich Schatzkammer[2], attributed to the Sarachi Workshop and to Annibale Fontana respectively.

Ewers with oval bodies with or without covers, standing on baluster stems and oval feet were much favoured by the Miseroni workshop, several examples in coloured hardstone are illustrated by Distelberger[3].

1.   R. Distelberger, "Beobachtungen zu den Steinschneidewerkstätten der Miseroni in Mailand und Prag", *Jahrbuch des Kunsthistorischen Sammlungen in Wien*, Vol. 74, 1978, p. 111, fig. 86.
2.   R. Distelberger, "Die Sarachi Werkstatt und Annibale Fontana", *Jahrbuch der Kunsthistorischen Sammlungen in Wien*, Vol. 71, 1975, figs. 143 and 144/6.
3.   See Note 1, figs. 87–90, 107–109.

J. H.

67 OVAL BOWL.
Workshop of Ottavio Miseroni, Milan, late XVIth century.

Heliotrope, the front end carved in low relief with a grotesque mask, the remainder with low relief scrolls terminating in volutes, the separate foot secured to the bowl by a gold mount champlevé enamelled opaque blue and white.

Dimensions: H. 10.5 × 19.3 cm

This cup was originally completed with enamelled gold mounts, en suite with that at the base of the bowl, around the upper rim and the foot, the unpolished edges show where the mounts were originally placed. Similar bowls attributed to the Miseroni workshops are in the Louvre and the Kunsthistorisches Museum, Vienna[1], of jasper and heliotrope respectively.
From the collection of William Beckford, Fonthill Heirlooms, no. 488.

1. R. Distelberger, "Beobachtungen zur den Steinschneidewerkstätten der Miseroni in Prag", *Jahrbuch der Kunsthistorischen Sammiungen in Wien*, Vol. 74, 1978.

J. H.

68 ROCK CRYSTAL BOWL.
Bohemia, Prague (?), second half of the XVIth century.

Large vesica shaped bowl, the exterior carved on each side with a scallop
shell flanked by gadroons radiating outwards. S scroll handles of rock
crystal carved with leaves, the shaped oval foot carved in relief with conventional leaves. Enamelled gold mounts, the upper mounts of the handles
with panels of translucent red, the stem mounts enamelled black, the foot
ring with black running scrolls, interrupted by translucent green cartouches,
white border.
    Complete with original chamois leather lined case with gilt tooled borders.

     Dimensions: H. 14.5 × 32 cm

This cup shows a number of unusual features:
    1. Its exceptionally massive character and great weight.
    2. The form of the foot, which is of Mogul design and may have been
incorporated from an earlier piece when this cup was made.
    3. The survival of its original protective leather case.
    The gadrooned ornament of the bowl and generally heavy proportions
recall the manner of Ferdinand Eusebio Miseroni[1], the last member of the
family to work for the Habsburg Emperors in the Prague workshop in the
Hradschin Palace.

1.   R. Distelberger, "Dionysio und Ferdinand Eusebio Miseroni", *Jahrbuch der Kunsthistorischen Sammlungen in Wien*, Vol. 75, 1979, p. 169/188.

J. H.

69 CAMEO.
Italy (Milan?), early XVIIth century

An oval emerald cameo carved with a bust portrait of Christ, the head facing sinister, mounted in gold closed collet with rose diamond border, reeded gold hoop, the ring and rose diamond border, late XVIIIth century.

Dimension: H. of cameo 11 mm

This representation of Christ is more familiar in heliotrope cameos in which the red flecks in the hardstone are used to dramatic effect.

Emerald cameos of such early date are of great rarity. Like the hardstone cameos, this emerald can probably be attributed to a Milanese glyptic master of the early XVIIth century[1].

1. For similar hardstone cameos see Eichler-Kris, *Die Kameen im Kunsthistorischen Museum*, Vienna, 1927, catalogue nos. 415–20, pls. 59, 61.

Illustration enlarged   J. H.

70 EMERALD CAMEO.
Italy, late XVIIth or early XVIIIth century, the frame later.

Head of Apollo wearing a laurel wreath on a bandeau in his hair, after the antique, cut in an emerald of fine grass-green colour, now mounted in a gold frame set with brilliants.

Diameter of cameo: 23 mm

This cameo is said to have formed part of a set of three, the others being Mars and Hermes. The representation is probably based on an idealised Hellenistic portrait of Alexander the Great, perhaps from a coin.

This cameo with the two others was presented by Augustus II, King of Poland and Elector of Saxony (1696–1733) to his illegitimate daughter by Countess Cosel, on her marriage in 1730 to Count John Moyszynski. It has remained in the family ever since. The whereabouts of the two other cameos from the set is not known.

Illustration enlarged   L. d'U.

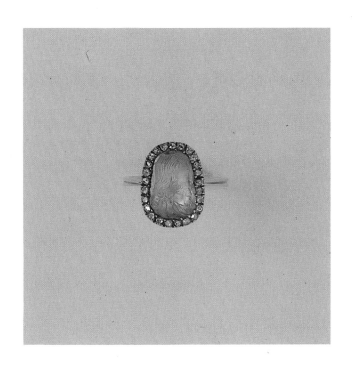

71 PLATTER.
German, probably Saxon.

Serpentine, with wide rim, the depression centering on a slightly recessed circle.

Diameter: 33.7 cm

Anonymous Loan   J. H.

72 FLASK.
Saxony, XVIIth century.

Serpentine body turned with spiral fluting, upper mount of pewter with screw thread to accept pewter screw top, loop handle cast and chased with foliage.

Dimension: H. 24 cm

A similar vase is published by E. von Philippovich; it is in a private collection and dated c. 1600[1].

1.   E. von Philippovoch, *Kuriositäten Antiquitäten*, Brunswick, 1966, p. 308, fig. 201.

J. H.

74 c

WAXES

---

73 PORTRAIT OF TITIAN.
    Italy, second half of the XVIth century.

    Coloured wax.

    The aged painter, in profile to the right, holds a handkerchief in his left hand
    and a portrait of his son in his right. Inscription at the top: *TITIAN
    PICT. ET FILII EFIGIES*.

        Diameter: 13 cm (with contemporary frame)

    This is an exceedingly fine modelled portrait which resembles the work of
    Giovanni Antonio De Rossi (Milan 1517–Rome, *post* 1575). Rossi was a
    cameo-engraver, medallist and wax modeller. The attribution is based on
    two wax portraits of Pius V by Rossi, one of which was in the Rosenheim
    Collection and the other, still as a Cardinal, in the Pyke Collection[1].
        The finely modelled faces of these two signed waxes and their resemblance
    in style to the one exhibited make the attribution acceptable.

    1.   E. Kris, *Renaissance Kleinkunst in Italian*, fig. 317, when the wax was in the Simon
          Collection in Berlin. Kris does not mention that the wax appeared in the Simon
          catalogue. A further reference to the wax is in A. Hess, *Antiquitäten Sammlung,*
          Frankfurt, October, 1912.

                                                                          E. J. P.

74 THREE PORTRAITS OF LADIES.
Italy, second half of the XVIth century.

Coloured wax.

(a) Profile to the right on slate ground.
(b) Profile to the left on green leather ground.
(c) With arms crossed on the chest, looking to the right.

      Diameters (with contemporary frames):
      (a) 14.5 cm (b) 13.5 cm (c) 10 cm

These portraits are most probably the work of Antonio Abonio (the younger) 1538–1597, who was born in Riva di Trento and died in Vienna. He was a medallist, who learnt his art in the Milanese School. He is regarded as having begun or been responsible for the transition from sketch-models to portraiture in wax. Abondio was a pupil of Leone Leoni, c. 1509–1590, who did not sign his works because of the convention that an artist should not place his signature in close proximity to the portraits of exalted personages. The quality and very fine workmanship of the three waxes bear such close resemblance to the waxes in some Museums[1], that an attribution to Abondio is reasonable.

1.   Museo Civico, Padua; Historisches Museum, Dresden; Bayerisches Nationalmuseum, Munich. The finely detailed modelling and jewelling all help in attribution.

E. J. P.

74a

74b

75　MODEL FOR A MEDAL OF THE MARQUESS OF TRIVICO.
Italy, third quarter of the XVIth century.

White wax.

Recto. In profile to the right. Inscription: *.FERD.LOFFREDVS.MARCH. TRIVICI.*
Verso. A woman presenting a lance to an armed warrior crowned with laurel who points out· the Marquess of Trivici to another warrior. Inscription: *DIVIQ.CARO.CAES.VERITAS.*

Diameter: 10 cm (with original frame)

This is the original model for a medal which is illustrated in P. A. Gaefani's *Museum Nazzuchellianum*[1] and fully described by A. Armand[2] who specifies that Fernando Loffredo, Marquess of Trivico, had been governor of Southern Italy and he was still alive in 1570.

1.　Venice, 1761–68. LXXXI, pl. no. 3.
2.　A. Armand, *Les Médailleurs Italiens,* Paris, 1885, Vol. II, p. 164. The inscription on the medal (diameter 68 mm) is identical to ours. The author advances the possibility that the crowned warrior is the Emperor Charles V.

E. J. P.

143

76 PORTRAIT OF A GENTLEMAN AND HIS WIFE
AND A NEW-BORN BABY.
Southern Germany (?), late XVIth century.

Coloured wax.

The lady, in profile to the right, holds the baby in her arms; the husband is seen in profile to the left, looking at them.

Diameter: 15.5 cm (with contemporary frame)

The style of the dress suggests that this is a South German work, although as will be subsequently seen, it may be Danish or Norwegian. It could appear that the group is by Heinrich Rappost, the elder. Rappost was born in Nuremberg (date unknown) and died in Berlin in 1592, where he was active as a medallist, wax modeller and goldsmith, between 1579 and 1589. It is also possible that the work might be by G. H. Rapp (XVI/XVIIth century) who was Danish or Norwegian.

E. J. P.

77 SHELL WITH WAX RELIEFS.
Initialled under the pair of lovers: $R^O_T\,Ca$
Prague (?), end of the XVIth century.

The inside of the shell has been used to contain two bas-reliefs in coloured wax; one with three naked women embracing each other (the Three Graces ?); one with lovers taking leave of each other, near a dog (perhaps Venus and Adonis) and, to the right, Cupid seated on another dog. Views of the countryside and a town in the background. The shell can be closed by means of a silver-gilt hinge.

Dimensions: 6.5 × 7.5 cm

The erotic character of these small compositions and the refined quality of the reliefs, delicately coloured and with small pearls on the coiffure of the women, recalls the taste of the court of Prague where Rudolf II commissioned pictures by B. Spranger and bronzes by A. de Vries and other artists that recall the atmosphere of these precious scenes. On the other hand, stylistically, these waxes seem to date from the end of the XVIth century.

It has proved impossible to identify the wax modeller who initialled this work.

Illustration enlarged   A. G.-P.

147

78 MASK.
Florence, second half of the XVIth century.

Red wax on *paragone* marble ground in a gilt brass oval frame.

Dimensions: 14×11 cm

This grotesque mask, which seems to have been created as a model, is close to the style of Buontalenti. It has been suggested, although no documents have as yet been found to prove it, that Buontalenti provided designs for some of the sculptural details on porcelain produced in the Medici manufactory in Florence. What is certain is that he gave designs for some of the lapis-lazuli vases carved in Florence. Vasari, however, wrote in 1568 (as has already been noted by Liverani and Middeldorf) that "Bernardo turns to everything: as may be seen from his producing, in a brief space of time, porcelain vases that have all the excellence of perfect antique examples . . . that he makes fantastic pottery vases, and those in porcelain in the finest forms (Vasari, ed. Milanesi, VII, 615). Some examples among the various vases published by G. Liverani[1] may be compared with this wax.

We know, on the other hand, that Cencio della Nera – a goldsmith active in the late XVIth century for Francesco I and Ferdinand I in the Grand-ducal workshops – provided on various occasions models in wax for rock-crystal vases, ornaments for porcelain vessels and other sorts of precious objects. His last work, for instance, left unfinished in 1591, was a silver vase with two masks that kept in place the handle. Stylistically his work came in the sphere of Buontalenti and of the goldsmith J. Bylivelt, who, in his turn, executed in gold and enamel some objects that had been designed by Buontalenti[2].

1. *Catalogo delle porcellane dei Medici,* Faenza, 1936.
2. C. W. Fock, "Francesco I e Ferdinando I mecenati di orafi e intagliatori di pietre dure", *Le Arti del Principato Mediceo,* Florence, 1980, pp. 333, 346, 357.

A. G.-P.

79   A VIEW OF NAPLES.
Nikolas Engelbert Cetto (d. 1746).

The complicated iconographical programme of this wax bas-relief, which is modelled over glass, is meant to show the story of the wedding of Carlos of Bourbon and Maria Amalia of Saxony and the cities that were in some way connected with them: Madrid, home of Carlos' parents; Dresden, capital of Maria Amalia's parents; Jerusalem, of which Carlos claimed to be king; and Naples, the seat of the young sovereigns.

The first relief, which is the one exhibited[1] shows a general view of the city of Naples. Above some angels hold a scroll with a list of the 76 most famous buildings and sites of the city. In the centre two sirens present the coats-of-arms of Carlos and Maria Amalia while Neptune and female marine deities hold the crown and the sceptres of the sovereign in one hand and with the other hand they present their crowned effigies. Above, Fame holds two scrolls, on one of which is written in Latin "Charles King of Sicily, Jerusalem and Naples, son of Philip V, King of Spain born in 1716 and raised to the throne in 1735". (In 1734 he was already King of Naples). On the other, "Maria Amalia by the Grace of God, Queen of two Sicilies, daughter of Augustus III, King of Poland, Queen of Saxony, born in 1722, married in 1738". At the extreme right some sirens and tritons hold the royal coat of arms beneath putti with a scroll bearing the name of the city of Naples. On the left a triton holds a shell on which is written in Latin, "the Mediterranean Sea". At the extreme left the signature *Nico. Engel. Cetto/Tittmoning. fecit.*

The central bas-relief was surrounded by ten small oval medallions of which only two remain, one depicting a view of the Piazza di Spagna in Naples and the other, which has lost its inscription, showing the harbour of the city.

Dimensions: Frame 97 × 57 × 21 cm; Relief: 44.5 × 55.5 cm

The series is completed by three other bas-reliefs (not exhibited here) which are described for greater clarity.

The second bas-relief showing Madrid is surmounted by a cartouche which lists the main buildings of the city; also visible is Fame with the legend *HIC STITORIA (sic) MUNDI* and, in the middle God the Father with the symbolic pelican; another cartouche surmounted by the royal crown bears the name of "Don Phelipe de Borbon Rey de Espana . . . Phelipe V Rey de Castilla, de Leon . . .". The main scene shows the Spanish provinces, including America and Africa, kneeling obediently, as well as the various coats of arms of the kingdoms and the Golden Fleece. The small lateral scenes, which have minute inscriptions explaining them, tell the story of Philip V, from the time when, as Duke of Anjou, he was appointed to succeed Charles II in 1700 (1). Then we see a "customary bullfight in Madrid" (2); the sovereign's entry into his capital (3); the King handing over "the kingship to his son in 1724" (4) (this was to Luis I who reigned for a very short while); the King who "after the death of his son in Sept. 1724 resumed the throne" (5); the "Departure of Don Carlos for Italy in 1731" (6); a "view of Madrid from the Toledo Gate" (7); a ceremony with the princes of Spain and Porto in 1729

(8); "Philip V making peace with the Emperor at Vienna in 1725" (9) and "Philip V of Spain taking the oath 20 May 1701" (10).

The third bas-relief of Jerusalem describes minutely the buildings of the city, giving particular importance to religious monuments, such as the Church of the Presentation of the Virgin, the Church of the Ascension, the Chapel on Mount Calvary, the tomb of the Virgin and of Christ and the Church of St. Francis. The various persons in the foreground represent different rulers: Constantine, "called the Great and the 1st Emperor who coming from Sicily took the first Jerusalem and the Catholic religion under his rule", and then the knights of St. John "who had all been born in Naples"; "Godfrey de Bouillon the first Christian and Catholic King", "Frederick II Roman Emperor", "Luigi King of All Sicily". The small oval scenes round the frame show the principal sites of the city: the Church where Christ was born at Nazareth, the interior; Bethlehem "now a monastery"; the Chapel on Mount Calvary; Mount Calvary with a Carmelite monastery; the Garden of Gethsemane; part of the new town with the Temple of Solomon; the place where Christ was crucified, etc.

The fourth panel, of Dresden, is crowned by the usual cartouche supported by angels, with the list of the main buildings of the Saxon capital (the Church of the Holy Cross, the Arsenal, the Powder Tower, the New Church of the Madonna, the Albea Gate, the Castle, the Theatre, the Church of St. Sophia, the Zwinger, various bridges and bastions, etc.). The main view shows the "parade camp drawn up by H.M. Frederick Augustus in 1730", with the names of the chief personages who include, besides the King, the Hereditary Prince, the Count of Saxony, and various other princes and attendants, with the description of the encampment, the tents, the stables, etc. The small oval views include the illumination of the Palace of the Count von Brühl, the "departure from the Royal Palace of Granja and the entry of the Conde Fuenclara Ambassador of their Majesties of Spain and Naples preceded by the Fries", with various other palaces bedecked and illuminated for the wedding of Maria Amalia. The second and the third bas-reliefs are signed respectively: *N . . . co Engelb . . . Fecit* 1740 and *Nico Engl. Fecit Titt.* The fourth panel is not signed.

Nikolas Engelbert Cetto, author of these works, was born at Tittmönig, in Southern Germany, the son of Johann Baptist Cetto, himself a modeller in wax. He died in 1746. E. J. Pyke[2] lists very few works by this artist: two which were in the Köhler Collection in Vienna, and two others auctioned some years ago in London. To this we can add four biblical scenes, smaller than those exhibited, belonging to the collections of the Spanish Patrimonio Nacional and exhibited in the Casita del Principe at the Escorial (they are signed *N. Engels* and *Ni. Eng. Cetto*, and are, as far as we know, still unpublished).

The prodigious technique of Cetto derives probably from his father Johann Baptist, whose *Battle Scene* (Munich, Bayerisches Nationalmuseum), is made of the same type of white wax. For a more naturalistic effect he covered the wax with fragments of foliage and human hair. The frames enclosing the bas-reliefs exhibited here do not seem contemporary: they indicate a taste already touched by neo-classicism of the kind that this style took in Spain. It is likely that older and severer frames (like those of the

(detail)

biblical scenes in the Escorial, with simple dark mouldings enriched by gold) may have been replaced by the present frames towards the end of Charles III's reign or during that of Charles IV. The provenance of all these pieces, probably royal, is at present a mystery.

1. Catalogue *Civiltà del' 700 a Napoli*, Florence, 1979.
2. E. J. Pyke, *A Biographical Dictionary of Wax Modellers*.

A. G.-P.

81

SCULPTURE

80 A PAIR OF MARBLE BUSTS: CARACALLA AND GETA.
Rome, IIIrd century; XVIIth century embellishments.

The bust of Caracalla is all original except for the nose which is an addition; the neck has been re-attached to the torso but all the parts in white marble appear ancient. The *paludamento* in oriental alabaster which hangs from his left shoulder dates from the Baroque period like the socle of *porta santa* marble. Only the head of Geta is ancient (down to the middle of the neck), the surface of the marble has suffered some wear and the nose has been repaired; the cloak in oriental alabaster is a baroque addition while the socle is in *africano* marble.

Dimensions: each H. 78 cm (with the socle)

Marcus Aurelius Antonius (186–217), called Caracalla, was the eldest son of the Emperor Septimus Severus and of his wife Julia Domna. He was born in Lyon while his younger brother Geta Publius Septimius (189–212) was born in Milan. In 198 Geta received the title of Caesar and in 209 those of Imperator and Augustus although he was the youngest brother. However, at their father's death at York in 211, Caracalla and Geta were proclaimed co-emperors and returned to Rome. In 212, Caracalla murdered his brother to secure the power for himself alone and later put to death about 20,000 men who had supported Geta: it is not surprising that he was considered *de natura truculentus* by an ancient writer, a sign of character and temperament that is obvious in most of his portraits. This emotional and violent rendering of the *natura* of an emperor was a new approach to portraiture in Roman art. As Caracalla, whose hate didn't end with his brother's death, proclaimed Geta's *damnatio memoriae*, the latter's portraits are relatively rare and this may explain why ours has suffered more. Caracalla was murdered in 217 by order of Macrinus the prefect of the praetorian guard who succeeded him.

The Caracalla bust presents many affinities with the Emperor's portrait in Berlin which is considered to be one of the best portraits of the period by Bernouilli[1]. The bust of Geta is quite close stylistically to the effigy of the Emperor in the Museo Nazionale Romano: both busts must have been made during the early youth of Geta as his beard was much longer in the last years of his life (this we know only through coins as no bust of this type remains)[2].

Ancient busts were eagerly collected during the Renaissance and the Baroque period: they were not only used to adorn the palaces of sovereigns but also as objects for the *Wunderkammer* (there is still an *antiquarium* with many busts – some ancient, some more recent imitations – in the Residenz in Munich and in Schloss Ambras).

A bust of Geta and a smaller bust of Caracalla (see note 1) were preserved in the famous Museo Kircheriano.

1.   J. J. Bernouilli, *Die Bildnisse der Römischen Kaiser*, Stuttgart, Berlin, Leipzig, 1894, Vol. III, pp. 51, 54, pl. XX.
2.   B. M. Felletti Maj, *Museo Nazionale Romano, I Ritratti*, Rome, 1953, pp. 133–134, fig. 264.

A. G.-P.

81 TWO MARBLE BUSTS OF HADRIAN AND L. AELIUS CAESAR (?).
Rome, second half of the XVIIth century.

The heads are in white marble, the *paludamenti* in various coloured marbles (*giallo antico, rosso antico,* various types of alabaster).

Dimensions: each H. 75 cm (without socles)

Busts of this type were made all through the late Renaissance, Baroque and Neoclassical period in Rome; their quality varies but some like the ones exhibited can be of fine craftsmanship. Many well known sculptors such as Bernini, Algardi and Duquesnoy were also restorers of antiques and some had assistants who were able to complete series of Emperors and other ornamental groups. This type of sculpture figured in a *Wunderkammer* or formed part of the furnishings of great palaces. Many are still preserved today, for example in the Palazzo Colonna, while Ficoroni, writing in 1744[1], recalls that "nel Palazzo Chigi al Corso" there was "una galleria di busti moderni ed alcuni antichi" which suggests that for the man of the Baroque era, what mattered most was the effect of the ensemble.

Whilst the identification of one of the busts with the Emperor Hadrian (reigned 117–138), based on well-known prototypes is not in doubt, the second of the younger man, is more problematic; he may be L. Aelius Caesar, who was Hadrian's adoptive son and died before him, or the young Marcus Aurelius who was Aelius' son and became Emperor after Antoninus Pius.

1.   F. dei Ficoroni, *Le singolarità d'Roma moderna ricercate e spiegate,* Rome, 1744, II, p. 63.

A. G.-P.

82 BOYS PLAYING THE GAME OF SACCOMAZZONE.
Italy, early XVIIth century, after Orazio Mochi (d. 1625).

Bronze, dark patination, inscribed on the rock and on the sole of a shoe no. 36.

Dimensions: H. 44.5 cm; L. 33 cm

This vigorous genre group of two peasant boys in rough, country attire playing a variety of blind man's bluff was modelled by Orazio Mochi and, according to Baldinucci[1], was reproduced in wax, plaster and bronze, as well as in marble on a monumental scale for the Boboli Gardens by Romolo Ferrucci[2]. The subject matter is derived from Giambologna's genre bronze statuettes of the *Bagpiper*, *Shepherd* and *Fowler*, invented towards the end of the XVIth century, under the influence of Bruegel and Dürer, to meet a demand at the court of the Medici for amusing, rustic caprices.

The inventory number 36 is that of the French Crown collection, in which the bronze appeared during the reign of Louis XIV[3], described as: "Un group de deux figures qui ont les yeux bandez et qui joüent à la seca, vulgairement dit Collin-maillard."

1. F. Baldinucci, *Notizie dei professori del Disegno* . . . , (ed. Ranalli, Florence, 1845–47, IV, p. 423.
2. J. Montagu, *Bronzes*, London, 1963, p. 90, fig. 98; F. Gurrieri and J. Chatfield, *Boboli Gardens,* Florence, 1972.
3. J. Guiffrey, *Inventaire général du Mobilier de la Couronne sous Louis XIV,* Paris, II, 1886, p. 34, no. 36.

Other versions: Kunsthistorisches Museum, Vienna (reproduced in colour by Montagu, *op. cit.*); Robert Strauss collection (sale Christie's, 3rd May, 1977, lot 97); Palazzo Venezia, Rome (exhibited in *Meesters van het Brons der Italiaanse Renaissance,* Amsterdam, 1961–62, no. 126); Victoria and Albert Museum, London (A 20–1956); Grenoble Museum; Louvre; coll. Prof. E. A. Maser, Chicago (repro. H. R. Weihrauch, *Europäische Bronzestatuetten,* Brunswick, 1967, fig. 283, and p. 507, no. 273); Liechtenstein collection (Stadtpalais, Vienna), half destroyed in the Second World War, is now in the Museum des Kunst-Handwerks, Leipzig; Straubing, Bavaria, private collection; Dr. A. von Frey collection (Paris art market, 1960).

Lent by M. Jacques Petit-Horry, Paris.   C. A.

83   JUNO AND MERCURY.
Florentine, early XVIIth century.
By Ferdinando Tacca (1619–1686).

Bronze, dark patination, inscribed on the back of the rock, No. 179.

Dimensions: H. 44 cm; W. 37 cm

The bronze came from the collection of André Le Nôtre, then passed to King
Louis XIV and into the French Royal Collection.

The number engraved on the group identifies it as one listed in the
Inventaire des bronzes de la Couronne of 1791: "Junon assise et Mercure découvrant
un vase qu'il tient sous son bras gauche". The subject and description also
correspond with a bronze listed in the inventory prepared in 1684 of bronzes
in the collection of the Este Dukes of Ferrara in a casino outside Modena;
"Un Mercurio con vaso in mano avanti a una figura di donna coronata
posta a sedere"[1]. The present bronze came into the French Crown collection
as a bequest from the estate of André le Nôtre to King Louis XIV, appearing
in Le Nôtre's inventory as "Un (groupe) de Junon et Mercure"[2]. Because
of an approximate correspondance between the subjects listed together in
the Parisian collections and that at Modena, Landais surmised that Le Nôtre
had acquired his set from the Duke of Ferrara[3]. As a result of much research
and identification of all the remaining subjects in both groups, Radcliffe
has recently established that this was not in fact the case and that there were
two separate, though similar, holdings of bronzes by Ferdinando Tacca in
Paris and Modena[4].

It follows that Le Nôtre probably acquired the present bronze more or
less directly from the Florentine studio of Ferdinando Tacca.

There are two other versions, one of which may have come from Modena:
Walker Art Gallery, Liverpool, bought on the London art market (H. 43.2
cm); Germanisches Nationalmuseum, Nuremberg (Inv. no. Pl. O. 2826;
acquired as a work by Johann Gregor van der Schardt)[5].

1.   *Documenti inediti per servire alla storia dei musei d'Italia,* Florence, 1878–80, III, 1880,
     p. 26, under the heading: 'Statue e figure di bronzo o metallo, molte delle quali erano
     a Sassuolo' in the 'Inventario delle statue di marmo e di bronzo, delle miniature ecc.,
     che sono al presente nel Casino di S.A. Ser. ma fuori di Porta Castello a. 1684'.
2.   H. Landais, "Sur quelques statuettes léguées par Le Nôtre à Louis XIV et conservées
     au Départment des objets d'art", in *Bulletin de Musées de France,* XIV, 1949, no. 3,
     pp. 60–63.
3.   Idem, *Les Bronzes Italiens de la Renaissance,* Paris, 1958, pp. 88–89.
4.   A. F. Radcliffe, "Ferdinando Tacca, the missing link in Florentine Baroque bronzes",
     in *Kunst des Barock in der Toskana,* Munich, 1976, esp. pp. 15–19 and note 10.
5.   Radcliffe, *op. cit.,* 1976, note 20 and fig. 5.

Lent by M. Jacques Petit-Horry, Paris   C. A.

84 A WALKING HORSE.
Workshop of Severo Calzetta da Ravenna (active pre-1504 to pre-1543).

Bronze, black lacquer.

Dimensions: H. 17 cm; L. 17 cm

The style and facture of this unusual statuette of a horse are those of Severo
da Ravenna. It is derived from the Hellenistic gilt bronze horses on the
façade of St. Mark's, Venice, though the mane is not hogged like theirs[1].
Inkstands from Severo's workshop with reductions of the equestrian statue
of Marcus Aurelius in Rome are known, and the appearance of the present
horse confirms his – and his humanist clients' – interest in antique sculpture.

1.   Exhibition Catalogue, *The Horses of San Marco,* Royal Academy, London, 1979.

C. A.

85 NEGRO-HEAD LAMP ON CLAW FOOT.
Workshop of Severo Calzetta da Ravenna (active pre-1504 to pre-1543).

Bronze gilt.

   Dimension: H. 24 cm

This is an exceptionally fine example of a well-known type of oil lamp
emanating from Padua at the turn of the XVth and XVIth centuries which
used to be attributed on general stylistic grounds to Andrea Riccio[1]. It has
since become clear that this class of lamps, together with many related
types, probably came from the workshop of Severo da Ravenna, with
whose emerging *oeuvre* there are close stylistic and technical parallels.
Such lamps are built up from separately cast components screwed together,
and minor variations in detail are therefore common.

1.   Cf. L. Planiscig, *Andrea Riccio,* Vienna, 1927, p. 181, fig. 199.

Anonymous Loan   C. A.

86 AN INKSTAND FORMED AS A KNEELING SATYR WITH A
BUCKET, SNAKES AND FOLIAGE.
After Severo Calzetta da Ravenna (active pre-1504 to pre-1543).

The satyr clearly supported a missing object in his bent right hand, though not the disparate celestial globe with which he appeared in the Strauss collection. The triangular base with architectural mouldings, acanthus rinceaux and ball feet is typical of Severo's production but the bucket, snakes and foliage are a separately cast component and do not appear elsewhere in Severo's oeuvre. The modelling and chiselling are characteristic of Severo at his best.

Dimensions: H. 23 cm

The satyr is closely related to an unpublished but initialled example from a private collection[1]. The emergence of the signed version – only the second known signed bronze by Severo – corroborates recent scholarly attempts to disassociate the model from the oeuvre of Riccio, to whom (or to whose workshop) have traditionally been attributed both this and the other main versions, e.g. Rome, Museo di Palazzo Venezia, formerly Barsanti collection[2]; Berlin, Kunstgewerbemuseum[3]; and New York, Samuel H. Kress Foundation[4]. The satyrs are generically related to the more subtly conceived ones at the angles of Riccio's *Paschal Candelabrum* in the Basilica of Sant' Antonio, Padua (1506–16), but their style, facture and mood differ markedly. In his review of the exhibition of Italian bronze statuettes held in London, Amsterdam and Florence in 1961–62, Pope-Hennessy began the process of elimination from Riccio's oeuvre of one example of this model – that in Rome – deeming it however to be a "counterfeit"[5]. In his catalogue of the Kress collection, however, he still listed their example under the name of Riccio, as he also did the compositionally related inkstand group of *Atlas supporting the Globe of the Heavens* in the Frick collection[6].

1. Christie's, London, 8th July, 1981: initialled SE under the groin.
2. *Meesters van het brons der Italiaanse Renaissance*, Amsterdam, 1961–62, no. 56; cf. H. R Weihrauch, *Die Bildwerke in Bronze* . . . , Munich, 1956, no. 86, with list of further versions.
3. No. K4300; cf. K. Pechstein, *Bronzen und Plaketten*, Berlin, 1968, no. 70, with list of versions.
4. No. L. 80: cf. J. Pope-Hennessy, *Renaissance Bronzes from the Samuel H. Kress Collection*, London, 1965, no. 473, fig. 486; L. Planiscig, *Andrea Riccio*, Vienna 1927, fig. 380 (cf. figs. 381–2).
5. "An Exhibition of Italian Bronze Statuettes", in *The Burlington Magazine*, CV, 1963, p. 21, *Essays on Italian Sculpture*, London, 1968, p. 178.
6. J. Pope-Hennessy, *The Frick Collection*, III, pp. 106–111.

C. A.

87 A WILD MAN OF THE WOODS.
Nuremberg, early XVIth century.
Workshop of Paulus Vischer (1498–1531).

Bronze, dark patination, the infant cast separately and possibly later (cylindrical marble base).

    Dimension: H. 20.5 cm

This model came from the Riedinger collection, Augsburg (sold Munich, 1894, lot 225); Guido von Rhò collection, Vienna[1]; Robert von Hirsch collection, Basle (sold Sotheby's, London, 22nd June, 1978, lot 324).
    An almost identical model is in the Staatliches Museum, Berlin-Dahlem[2]. Another is in the Carrand collection in the Museo Nazionale (Bargello), Florence.

1.   E. Braun, *Die Bronzen der Sammlung Guido Von Rhò in Wien*, Vienna, 1908, pl. XXXVI; E. F. Bange *Die Deutschen Bronzestatuetten des 16. Jahrhunderts*, Berlin, 1949, no. 68.
2.   Inv. no. 8403; 20 cm high; cf. C. Theuerkaut, in *Der Mensch um 1500*, exhibition catalogue, Berlin, 1977, no. 29, fig. 126.

                  C. A.

88 EQUESTRIAN STATUETTE OF KING LOUIS XIII OF FRANCE.
Hubert le Sueur (c. 1585–post 1658).

Bronze, signed on saddle-girth *LE SVEVR*.

Dimensions: H. 20.5 cm; L. 19 cm

The discovery of this signed statuette by Le Sueur was important, for it served to link with his name a number of other equestrian bronzes which had previously not been satisfactorily attributed. A comparison of the horse and rider with Le Sueur's monumental equestrian statue of King Charles I now in Trafalgar Square, signed and dated 1633, corroborates the evidence of the die-struck signature. There is a statuette identical in all particulars except for the separately cast head in the Victoria and Albert Museum (A. 108–1956), whose features are not unlike those of Philip II of Spain, though the identification is not conclusive. A bigger version of the portrait of Louis XIII is also in the Victoria and Albert Museum, paired with a rearing equestrian statuette of King Henri IV (A. 47–1951). All are discussed in the articles cited in the Bibliography. The treatment is derived at second hand from the equestrian statues of Giambologna and Pietro Tacca produced in the last decade of the XVIth century in the Grand-Ducal studio in Florence. It is unclear whether the statuettes of French monarchs were produced before or after Le Sueur left Paris to enter the service of King Charles I, though it is likely that the models for the portrait heads were taken while he was in the service of the French crown.

General Bibliography:
C. Avery, "Hubert le Sueur's Portraits of King Charles I in Bronze, at Stourhead, Ickworth and Elsewhere", in *National Trust Studies,* I, 1979, pp. 143; C. Avery, A. Radcliffe and M. Leithe-Jasper, *Giambologna, ein Wendepunkt der Europäischen Plastik*, Vienna, 1978, no. 163f.

C. A.

89 HERCULES AND A CENTAUR.
    Italy, early XVIIth century.
    After Giambologna (1529–1608).

Gilt bronze, marble base.

    Dimensions: H. 37.5 cm; W. 31 cm

The subject is described in early sources as in the title above, and later identifications of the centaur as Nessus are incorrect, for Hercules shot him with a bow and arrow. The original version of the composition was cast in silver by Giambologna[1] after 1576 and was one of the six *Labours of Hercules* mounted on the *studiolo* of the Grand-Duke Francesco I de'Medici in the newly-built Tribuna of the Uffizi (since lost). The original model was two-thirds of a *braccio* high, as was the earliest recorded example in bronze, that by Antonio Susini in the inheritance of Lorenzo Salviati in 1609.

    The present bronze is closely related to a fine cast in the Kunsthistorisches Museum, Vienna (Inv. no. 5834) which is 40.2 cm high. According to Filippo Baldinucci, versions were also cast by Gianfrancesco Susini.

1.   C. Avery and A. Radcliffe *Giambologna, Sculptor to the Medici*, London (Arts Council), 1978, no. 81.

Anonymous Loan   C. A.

90 AN ARTICULATED BRONZE STATUETTE OF A NUDE MAN,
PERHAPS VULCAN.
Venetian or South German, late XVIth century.

Dimension: H. 70.5 cm

This highly unusual statuette was presumably an automaton striking the
hours on a bell with hammers in his articulated arms, and kicking it with
his right leg as well. His noble mien and stylised metallic wreath suggest
that he might have represented Vulcan, whose mythological hammering
of armour at a forge was analogous to the practical function of the statuette.

The articulation and undisguised nudity recall German Renaissance
wooden lay figures for artists, for example, those by the specialist master,
initialling I.P., who was active in Salzburg in the early XVIth century[1].
The suave treatment of anatomy and thin-walled casting point to a date
nearer the end of the century, but the place of origin is hard to define between
Venice and South Germany.

1.   J. Rasmussen, *Deutsche Kleinplastik der Renaissance und des Barock,* Museum für Kunst
      und Gewerbe, Hamburg, 1975, no. 6; C. Theuerkauff, in *Der Mensch um 1500,*
      exhibition catalogue, Staatliche Museum, Berlin, 1977, no. 30, p. 166f.

C. A.

91 BRONZE MEMENTO MORI.
Germany, second half of the XVIth century.

Dimension: H. 33.5 cm

The representation of the human body in decomposition has a long history
in European art: see, to give one example, the fresco with the Triumph of
Death, now attributed to Buffalmacco, in the Camposanto at Pisa[1].

In the XVIth century there was a revival of this Gothic tradition which
has its highest instance, in sculpture, in the tomb of René de Chalons by
Ligier Richier in the church of St. Pierre at Bar-le-Duc (c. 1544), where a
standing skeleton with shreds of flesh adhering to the bones is rendered with
almost ornamental virtuosity[2].

This bronze belongs to this same current of taste and style, with the human
body, though not entirely recognisable, not yet a skeleton, and seeming to
ask for divine pity with the gesture of the arms and the raised head. There is
another type of representation in which the skeleton, still partly covered with
flesh, stands rather for Death; an example of this other aspect of Time's
destruction is shown by an ivory exhibited a few years ago at Providence[3],
showing a skeleton holding an hour glass and the symbols of the ravages of
time, standing for the triumph of Death. There is also a figure in pear-wood
attributed to Hans Leinberger (active in Landshut, about 1520) in Schloss
Ambras, and a figure in box-wood, German and late XVIth century, in the
Walters Art Gallery, Baltimore. Other examples are in the Bayerisches
Nationalmuseum, Munich.

Stylistically our *memento mori* is close to an equestrian group in the Metro-
politan Museum, New York, attributed to a master of the Upper Rhine,[4] a
region between Meuse and Rhine, which seems to have felt especially the
fascination of the *ars moriendi*.

1. L. Bellosi, *Buffalmacco e il Trionfo della Morte,* Turin, 1974, fig. 20.
2. A. Blunt, *Art and Architecture in France 1500 to 1700,* Hammondsworth, 1953, fig. 57.
3. Catalogue of Exhibition *Europe in Torment: 1450–1550,* Providence, Rhode Island,
    1974, pp. 100–101.
4. E. F. Bange, *La piccola scultura in lego e pietre del Rinascimento tedesco,* pl. LXXI. Another
    cast of the exhibited bronze was with Sotheby's, 16th December, 1971, lot 105; for
    Baltimore, see *Treasures* . . . by A. Gabhart, Baltimore, 1971, p. 37. In painting, the
    pictures by Hans Baldung Grien in Basel and Ottawa should be recalled here.

A. G.-P.

92 A PAIR OF DOUBLE-HEADED EAGLES WITH CORONETS.
Nuremberg, late XVIth century.
Possibly from the circle of Wenzel Jamnitzer (1508–1588).

Gilt bronze (later bases).

Dimensions: H. 14.3 cm; L. 17.8 cm

The necessarily heraldic nature of the symbolic double-headed eagle is here
allied to a highly naturalistic rendering of the feathers and a life-like poise.
The painstaking chasing and gilding point to a South German origin in a
goldsmith's workshop. The eagles probably date from before 1602 as they
wear simple coronets and not the Rudolphine crown.

Anonymous Loan.   C. A.

LEAD PORTRAIT MEDAL OF THE EMPEROR CHARLES V.
Nuremberg, datable 1521.

Designed by Albrecht Dürer, the dies by Hans Kraft the Elder.

Obverse:
The youthful Emperor in profile to the right, wearing armour, the Imperial crown and the chain of the Order of the Golden Fleece, inscribed *CAROLVS: V: RO : IMPER:*, within a flanged border decorated with fourteen coats of arms of the Empire (*Reich*), Habsburg territories and the Kingdom.

Reverse:
The double-headed Imperial spread-eagle, (*Reichsadler*), with the date 1521 on plaques hanging from its beaks, within a flanged border decorated with thirteen coats of arms and a wreath with a capital N (for Nuremberg).

   Diameter: 5.5 cm

Albrecht Dürer's portrait medal of the young Emperor Charles V is considered to be perhaps the finest of the German Renaissance medals. It was commissioned by the City Fathers of Nuremberg for presentation to the Emperor on his holding the Diet there in 1521. In the event, this never took place as the Diet was held in Worms. According to material in the archives at Nuremberg[1], the council wrote to Lazarus Spengler, the Nuremberg town clerk, to the effect that Albrecht Dürer had designed the medal with advice from his friend, Willibald Pirkheimer, and that they would like him, consulting if necessary Johann Stabius, to provide confirmation that the complicated heraldic details involved were correct (Letter: Monday after Trinity – 6th June 1520).

   On the 17th February, 1521, the Council wrote to their representative in Worms informing him that the dies for this medal were now prepared and that they intended him to present the Emperor with 100 of these medals in silver. Further, they would like his advice as to a suitable date for the presentation in order to gain the maximum royal favour as they felt that it was the design and execution of the medal rather than the intrinsic value of the metal which they considered important. His reply must have been discouraging as in a further letter, dated 1st March, 1521, he is instructed to hold those medals already sent to him and to postpone the event.

   Early in 1521 Dürer mentions in his diary what might be one of these medals when he writes that he sent amongst other things "a silver Emperor" to Pirkheimer[2]. The bust of the Emperor is based on various portraits of his predecessor and grandfather Maximilian, notably those of Bernard Strigel, thus complying with official iconography of the Emperor which at the time was not fully developed for Charles V. That Hans Kraft the Elder engraved the dies is confirmed not only because he was engraver to the Nuremberg mint at the time but also because he had had the experience of engraving the dies for the smaller medal, which served as the precedent for this one, of

Frederick the Wise, which was designed by Lucas Cranach at Constance in 1507.

Provisional list of other surviving examples:

SILVER
1. Kunsthistorisches Museum, Vienna.
2. Kaiser Friedrich Museum, Berlin.
3. Münzkabinett, Munich.
4. Schloss Coburg.
5. Germanisches Museum, Nuremberg.
6. Gerard Hirsch Auction, Munich, 14–17th March, 1967, no. 501: DM. 26,500; ex-Horsky Collection, 1910, no. 865.
7. Museo Arqueológico Nacional, Madrid.
8. Bibliothèque Nationale, Paris.
9. Victoria and Albert Museum, London, 14 "stamped on the edge".
10. Reichmann and Co. Auktion, Halle, 5–6th July, 1921, lot 3. Silver ? A poor cast.
11. Richard Falkiner Collection, London. At present on loan to the Manchester City Art Gallery.

BRONZE
12. Kunsthistorisches Museum, Vienna.
13. Germanisches Nationalmuseum, Nuremberg.

LEAD
14. Wallace Collection, London.
15. National Gallery of Art, Washington D.C.
16. Adalbert von Lanna Sale – Lepke, Berlin, 16–19th May, 1911, lot 587.
17. John Tradescant, *Musaeum Tradescantianum*, London, 1656, para. XIV, describes one in copper or lead which is no longer in the Ashmolean Museum, Oxford.

The bronze medals listed might be lead as this metal sometimes reacts with its environment to give the superficial appearance of copper.

1. Dr. Hans Petz, *Jahrbuch für Kunstsammler* (Vienna), Vol. X.
2. J.-A. Goris and G. Marlier, *Albrecht Dürer, Diary of his journey to the Netherlands*, 1520–21, London, 1971, p. 85.

General Bibliography:
K. Domanig, *Die Deutsche Medaille*, Wien, 1907, no. 39; M. Bernhart, *Die Bildnismedaillen Karls des Fünften*, München, 1919, pl. VI, 62; G. Habich, *Die Deutschen Schaumünzen des XVI Jahrhunderts*, München, 1929/35, Vol. 1, p. 5, no. 18; C. Theuerkauft, in *Die Mensch um 1500*, exhibition catalogue, Staatliche Museum, Berlin, 1977, no. 4, figs. 39, 40.

Illustration enlarged   R. F.

94 PLAQUETTE.
South Germany, last quarter of XVIth century.

Gilt copper plaquette finely repoussé and chased with the scene of Moses
striking the rock, standing erect in the centre, as water gushes out into a
vase held by a kneeling maiden, a naked putto at her side with an empty
ewer, a man drinking in the background, to the far left a soldier with a ewer
in his hand.

Diameter: 5.5 cm

The elegant postures of the figures and the complex composition suggest the
influence of Etienne Delaune. This French Huguenot graphic master spent
some years in Munich and his designs had much influence on South German
goldsmiths.

   This plaquette was probably originally attached to a casket. It appears to
be unique, no cast version being recorded. A rectangular plaquette of this
subject after a model by Peter Flötner is, however, known and exists in many
examples[1], either built into goldsmiths' work or applied to cabinets.

1.   I. Weber, *Deutsche, Niederländische und Französische Renaissanceplaketten,* Munich, 1975,
      cat. no. 33,3.

Illustration enlarged   J. H.

95 A PORTRAIT MEDALLION OF A MAN IN A BERET AND ARMOUR.
Germany, early XVIth century.

Solnhofen stone, uniface (turned ebonised wood frame).

The warrior is richly attired in armour but with a torque on his beret and a
chain round his neck, both probably of gold. His identity is at present
unknown.

Diameter: 4.2 cm

Illustration enlarged   C. A.

189

96A A PORTRAIT MEDALLION OF FRIEDERICH BEHAIM.
Germany, early XVIth century.

Solnhofen stone (later wooden mount).

Obverse:
The subject in profile to the left wearing a cap, shirt and tunic, inscribed in relief round the rim: *FRIDERICH. PEHAIM. ALT. XXXV. IAR.*

Reverse:
Blank, apart from the monogram of Albrecht Dürer, A.D. and the date 1526 (printed paper label 450).

Diameter: 4 cm obverse

The monogram of Dürer on the reverse is not to be taken seriously and was frequently appended by others as a tribute even during his lifetime and particularly in the early XVIIth century. Such reliefs served as the master models for casting versions in metal by means of taking casts in plaster to form moulds.

Habich[1] gives the diameter of known casts as 39 mm.

Friedrich (VII) Behaim von Schwarzbach (1491–1533) was a town councillor of Nuremberg in 1518, as well as mayor (Bürgermeister) and councillor of war (Kriegsrat). He was specially concerned with religious problems. The normal reverse for this medal is dated 1526, which is correct for the given age of the subject and is presumably the reason for the date added to the spurious Dürer monogram on the back of the present uniface.

1. G. Habich, *Die deutschen Schaumünzen des XVI Jahrhunderts*, München 1929/35, I, 2, no. 936, pl. CXVI, 10 (with earlier literature and mention of the present piece).

C. A.

96B A MEDALLION WITH THE FURTENBACH ARMS.
Augsburg, early XVIth century.

Solnhofen stone, uniface (mounted in a wooden frame with no. 96A).

Carved with the coat of arms of the Furtenbach family of Augsburg: a bend wavy, the helm surmounted by a crest, two addorsed wings[1].

Diameter: 3.8 cm

1. E. Zimmermann, *Augsburger Zeichen und Wappen*, Augsburg, 1970, no. 1458.

C. A.

96b   96a

97A A PORTRAIT MEDALLION OF JOHANN GEUDER.
Nuremberg, 1526.
Perhaps by Matthes Gebel (active 1523, died 1574).

Solnhofen stone, uniface (mounted in a wooden frame with no. 10).

The subject in profile to the left, bare-headed, with beard and moustache, truncated at the neck, inscribed in relief round the rim: *IOANNES. GEVDER. AETATIS. SVAE. AN. XXX*[1].

Diameter: 4.5 cm

The normal reverse of the medal for which this is the obverse design shows a classical military trophy featuring a breastplate, above a shield and helm much as in the following item, with an inscription round the rim: *RECTE AGENDO NE TIMEAS MDXXVI*. Johann Geuder (1496–1557) was a town councillor of Nuremberg and became mayor (Burgermeister) in 1545. Son of Martin Geuder and Juliana Pirkamerin, he married on 4th July, 1519 Brigitta, daughter of Bernhard Hirssvogels and Barbara Imhof.

1. G. Habich, *Die deutschen Schaumünzen des XVI Jahrhunderts*, Munich, 1929–35, I, 2, no. 941, pl. CXV.

97B A MEDALLION WITH THE GEUDER ARMS.
Nuremberg, 1532.
Perhaps by Matthes Gebel (active 1523, died 1574).

Solnhofen stone, uniface (mounted in a wooden frame with no. 11).

Diameter: 2.7 cm

Within a laurel wreath lie a helm with an elaborate crest and a shield with the Geuder coat of arms[1]: a triangular diamond between three mullets of six points. In the field above an inscription in relief: *SOLA VIRTVS. M.D. XXXII.*

Plainly a design for the reverse of a medal of one of the Geuder family, but not recorded in the standard reference work of Habich, *Die deutschen Schaumünzen*.

1. E. Zimmermann, *Augsburger Zeichen und Wappen*, Augsburg, 1970, no. 1925.

C. A.

97b   97a

98 THE PROPHET HOSEA (?) WITH A WOMAN AND CHILDREN.
Peter Flötner (d. 1546).

Solnhofen stone.

The precision and brilliance of carving prove that this plaque is the original
model by Peter Flötner for one of his series of allegorical plaquettes, better
known from casts in lead[1].

Dimensions: H. 6 cm; W. 8.4 cm

The exact meaning is obscure. A woman in voluminous robes standing
centrally points to a rainbow in the upper right hand corner appearing over
a river landscape dotted with buildings. She holds with her left hand a naked
baby boy; while a naked baby girl and another child on the right brandish
a bunch of grapes; at the left a rather older child clad in a shirt drinks from a
flask. A bearded man, heavily robed, steps forward between the woman
and child and turns his head sharply to look at the rainbow, following her
pointing gesture. In the Behaim list it is cited as "The Prophet Hosea with a
whore and four children", referring to the Book of Hosea, I, v.2[2].

1. E. F. Bange, *Die Bildwerke in Bronzes und in anderen Metallen* . . . , Berlin, Leipzig, 1923,
no. 5685, pp. 88–89: lead cast, from the former Kunstkammer, 7 cm × 9.3 cm; I. Weber,
Die Deutsche, Niederländische und Französische Renaissanceplaketten, 1500–1600, Munich,
1975, no. 51 (with list of examples in metal and discussion of the subject).
2. "The beginning of the word of the Lord by Hosea, And the Lord said to Hosea,
Go, take unto thee a wife of whoredoms and children of whoredoms: for the land
hath committed great whoredom, departing from the Lord."

C. A.

99 A PORTRAIT MEDALLION OF A MAN.
    Germany, dated 1594.

Solnhofen stone (octagonal ebonised wood frame with various labels on reverse).

Obverse:
The subject in profile to the right, bare-headed, with beard and moustache and wearing a ruff, inscribed in relief round the rim *DANIEL PLACOTOMVS DANTISCA: AET: 28*, and with incised date on the shoulder 1594.

Reverse:
Manuscript lower case inscription in six lines, *Tobias Werner hat dieses gemacht welchen anfangs nur ein Töpfer gewesen.*

Diameter: 3.1 cm

The classicizing word "Placotomus" is hard to interpret but may be a translation of a surname or occupation such as Steinschneider (=stone-cutter or engraver) by a combination of the Greek noun PLAX meaning a flat-stone and TOMOS meaning cutting. "Dantisca" is the Latin form of the name Danzig.

Illustration enlarged   C. A.

100 A DRAUGHTSMAN CARVED WITH AN EAGLE POUNCING ON
A HARE.
Germany, XIIth to XIIIth century.

Morse ivory (?).

The bird of prey stands over the hare, its neck following the curve of the
field and its wing counterpointing it: the hare is crushed by the impact and
cowers in fear at the lower edge. The whole is set within a wide rim carved
with a basketwork or woven motif.

    Diameter: 5.2 cm

Illustration enlarged   C. A.

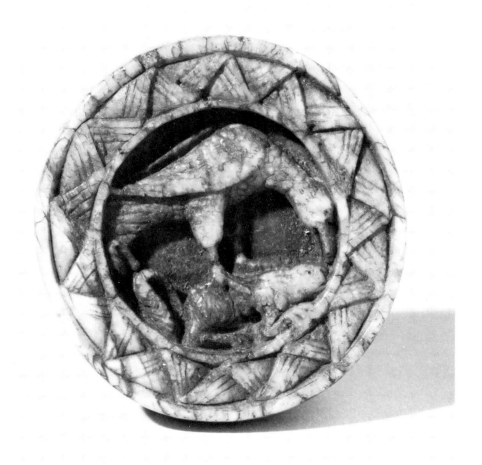

101 A HOUSE ALTAR WITH EPISODES FROM THE LIFE OF CHRIST.
Italian, XVth century.

From the Embriachi workshop.

Wooden carcase, with carved bone plaques and wood and bone intarsia.
(XVIth century ivory Corpus Christi).
   The episodes read chronologically from the lower left, Annunciation;
Nativity with Adoration of the Shepherds; Adoration of the Magi; Betrayal;
Crucifixion.

   Dimensions: H. 84.5 cm; W. 44 cm

This house-altar is a fine and characteristic example of the work produced
in Venice by the workshop of the Florentine carver Baldassare di Simone
d'Aliotto degli Embriachi (doc. active 1400–1409)[1].

1.   E. von Philippovich, *Elfenbein*, Brunswick, 1961, pp. 76–77, figs. 59–60.

                                                         C. A.

102 A MEDALLION CARVED WITH THE TEMPTATION OF ADAM
AND THE EXPULSION FROM THE GARDEN OF EDEN.
Germany, middle of the XVIth century.

Ivory, ajouré against a dark background and within a turned border with
concentric mouldings.

Obverse:
Adam and Eve are seated naked side by side under the Tree of Knowledge,
Eve proffering the apple, while the serpent looks down from above. In the
middle-ground to the left is an elephant and to the right a pair of deer
and some rabbits (symbolic of the lusts of the flesh) while a monkey
(symbolic of evil) squats on the ground at Adam's feet. The deeply moulded
turned rim protects the delicate surface of the carving.

Reverse:
The avenging angel bearing a sword and surrounded by an aura of light
enters from the left, driving the repentant Adam and Eve before him, past
some trees. This scene is smaller in diameter and appears to have been
separately carved and inserted into the moulded rim, which is wider than on
the obverse. Its style is, however, indistinguishable from that of the obverse
and its separate carving was probably a matter of technical convenience and
safety. The piece is similar to contemporary draughtsmen and might perhaps
have been used in a monastery.

Diameter: 5 cm

Illustration enlarged C. A.

103 EWER.
Germany. J. M. Maucher, Schwäbisch Gmund., second half of the XVIIth century.

Ivory, the oval barrel carved in high relief with a continuous band showing the Triumph of Bacchus, accompanied by nymphs and satyrs. Spout, handle and hinged cover carved of separate pieces of ivory, the handle terminating in a satyr emerging from an acanthus leaf, carved in the round, the cover with a grotesque mask, volute thumb-piece and acanthus finial.

Dimensions: H. 21.5 cm; W. 20 cm

Johann Michael Maucher (1645–1700), son of a gunstock-maker, worked at first in Schwäbisch Gmund, but went later to Augsburg and finally Würzburg. He specialised in carving ewers, basins and ivory plaques for insertion in gun and pistol stocks. After leaving Schwäbisch Gmund in 1688, to avoid arrest, he is said to have made an exceptionally fine gunstock for presentation to the Emperor Leopold I in order to gain his pardon. His work is widely represented in German museums, both in the form of vessels and gunmounts.

J. H.

WOOD CARVING

---

104 A STRING OF TWENTY-THREE BEADS CARVED WITH IMAGES
TAKEN FROM ANCIENT ROMAN SESTERTII.
Germany, early XVIth century.

Plumstones.

The designs on this string of beads carved on nutshells (a sort of secular
rosary, perhaps the equivalent of "worry beads") are taken from bronze
sestertii of ancient Rome; the initials "S.C." ("Senatus Consulto")
appearing on most of them show that the designs were bronze coins, the
authority for striking which was vested in the Senate, whereas the striking
of silver and gold coins was the prerogative of the Emperor.

Dimensions: (Each bead) 2.5 × 2 cm approximately

R. F.

105 A WALNUT CARVED WITH A VARIETY OF HUMAN FACES
AMIDST FOLIAGE.
Netherlands or Germany, early XVIth century.

Walnut shell (wire loop for suspension).

For other, similar pieces, see the collection of Adalbert von Lanna, Prague,
sale, Rudolph Lepke, Berlin, 21st–28th March, 1911, lots 170–171. Carvings
in whole walnut shells was a speciality of Antwerp.

Dimensions: H. 40 mm; W. 30 mm

C. A.

106 A WALNUT CARVED WITH SCENES FROM THE STORY
OF ORPHEUS.
Netherlands or Germany, early XVIth century.

Walnut shell (fitted with a silvered metal spout and spring-loaded cap).

Orpheus is shown seated and lightly draped playing a lute in a wooded
landscape with animals listening to his music. The fitted spout and cap suggest
that this walnut was used as a container for powder or sand for blotting
letters.

Dimensions: H. 50 mm; W. 25 mm

C. A.

105   106

107 A MEDALLION WITH THE STORY OF LOT AND HIS DAUGHTERS
IN A LANDSCAPE.
Germany, early XVIth century.

Boxwood, uniface (turned ebonised wood frame).

In the foreground, Lot and his two daughters are shown seated beneath
a tree. The daughters are dressed in the clothes of rich bourgeoises of the
early XVIth century. The first daughter, her bodice unlaced to reveal her
bosom, embraces her father with her left hand and with her right, offers him
wine in a jar. The other sister sits further back leaning her arm on a flask.
Lot wears a voluminous cloak of no recognisable period. In the background,
stretching right across the field, is a distant city, probably Sodom, with
Lot's wife turning back towards it presumably caught just before she was
turned into a pillar of salt. The carving is brilliantly incisive and the design
may well be derived from a contemporary print.

Diameter: 3.5 cm

Illustration enlarged   C. A.

108 AN ALLEGORICAL RELIEF OF RHETORIC AND ARITHMETIC DISPUTING.
South German, early XVIth century, after Hans Sebald Beham.

Boxwood, uniface (ebonised wood frame).

Beneath an arcade in the Renaissance style two allegorical female figures lightly draped are shown in attitudes of disputation: the one on the left representing Rhetoric stands beside a tablet propped on a desk and gestures with her hands in mid-air; the other, representing Arithmetic, shown frontally and standing in contrapposto indicates with her right hand a series of numbers 1–10 inscribed on a tablet held in her left hand. Below, on the floor are a set of nesting weights and two other larger ones. The compositions are reversed and reduced from two of a cycle of engravings of the Liberal Arts (nos. 3 and 4) by H. S. Beham of c. 1519[1]. The rhomboidal shape suggests that the plaque formed part of a larger complex, possibly a small box, with other similar plaques, no doubt based on Beham's other engravings.

Dimensions: H. 4.7 cm; W. (at top) 5.4 cm; (at bottom) 5.2 cm

1.   Bartsch, VIII 164, 123–4; Hollstein nos. 125–6. Our thanks to Dr. Jennifer Montagu, Warburg Institute, London University, for the identification of the subject and source.

Illustration enlarged   C. A.

109 A PORTRAIT MEDALLION OF DANIEL DE HANNA.
Germany, middle of the XVIth century.

Boxwood, uniface (rectangular ebonised wooden frame).

The subject in profile to the right, with close-cropped hair and trimmed
beard and moustache, shown in all *antica drapery*, inscribed in relief round
the rim: *DANIEL:DE:HANNA:MER:MAR:F:*

Diameter: 3.7 cm

Illustration enlarged   C. A.

110 BOXWOOD BAS-RELIEF WITH THE BATTLE OF ARBELA.
Johann Leonhard Baur (1681–1760).

The relief which has some gold and silver touchings is inscribed at lower
right: *ILB. DI IVLI.* and signed on the back: *I Leon: BAUR fec* (under the
signature an old inventory number in ink, 8858 co. p). The composition is
taken from Charles Lebrun's famous painting *The Battle of Arbela*, which
is part of a series dedicated to the story of Alexander the Great. These
enormous pictures were painted in the 1660s and Bernini, during his sojourn
in France 1665, admired two of them. *The Battle of Arbela*, which is today
in the Louvre, was probably finished about 1668, and in 1669 Sebastian
Bourdon referred to it in a public lecture in the Académie. The composition
shows Alexander on horseback with a sword in his hand trying to reach
Darius, seated on his throne holding a bow. The diviner Aristendes notices
the eagle flying above the head of the hero as a presage of victory[1].

Dimensions: 12.5 × 18.5 cm   A. G.-P.

Baur has shown prodigious ability in summarising Le Brun's enormous composition (4.70 × 12.65 m) to reduce it to the small size of a relief. Our panel must have formed part of a group and was obviously derived from engravings as, to our knowledge, Baur never visited Paris. In his Thieme-Becker entry on Baur, Christian Scherer[2] mentions a series of reliefs carved in wood by the artist after Lebrun's compositions which were lost. This is the first one to appear and as it is signed on the back there is no doubt about its authorship. It seems that Baur was also a goldsmith and a carver in ivory, mother-of-pearl and various types of wood. He was born in Augsburg, where there was a long tradition of this sort of precious work, and spent some of his life in Berlin. Some boxwood reliefs by him are (or were before the war) in the Löwenburg of Wilhelmshöhe in Kassel: one of them was signed and dated 1718.

1. Information taken from the catalogue of the exhibition *Charles Lebrun*, Versailles, 1963, p. 89, entry by J. Thuillier.
2. U. Thieme and F. Becker (ed.), *Allgemeines Lexikon der Bildenden Künstler,* Leipzig, 1909, (vol. III, p. 89).

A. G.-P.

III FRAME.
Netherlands, probably Antwerp, third quarter of XVIth century.

Boxwood, the front set with a (later) circular mirror, within a frame of tabernacle shape composed of interlacing strapwork, with lion masks at the intersections, enclosing bunches of fruit, flanked on each side by a putto holding a shield within an oval niche and, above, in an arched recess, a nude female figure symbolising justice; above and below the mirror a tablet with Latin inscription; the back carved with similar design, but centring on a circular relief of six men being devoured by lions in a pit while a seventh is suspended above, a King and four other men looking on; above in an arched niche, a nude man playing a viol. Above and below the central relief, two tablets, one with Dutch inscription, the second with the First Commandment in French.

Dimension: H 13.5 cm

The design is derived from a Flemish graphic source but a similar mirror case in the Wallace Collection (no. S 293) with inscriptions in four languages is signed *IN AUGUSTA* 1577, indicating that such cases were also carved in Augsburg.

J. H.

112 KNIFE AND FORK.
Netherlands, dated 1578.

Boxwood handles of rectangular section, carved and pierced in three stages, the knife with (1) a ring of dancing peasants; (2) a betrothal subject, and figures of warriors; (3) Justice and Faith with the owner's name and date, *B. POLANUS. ANNO* 1578, engraved silver ferrule, shaped single-edged blade, etched and gilt next to the handle; the fork with (1) dancing peasants; (2) a young knight at his prayers, a man being armed and figures of warriors; (3) Hope and Charity with the same name and date as the knife handle, two pronged fork, partly gilt, probably of later date than the handle.

Dimensions: L. of knife 25.3 cm; L. of fork 24.5 cm

J. H.

113   KNIFE.
Netherlands, probably Antwerp, late XVIth century.

The boxwood handle of rectangular section carved with four reliefs within arched niches enclosing Bathsheba at the bath, David with his harp, a man slaying a lion with a sword and David with the head of Goliath, the sides carved with Venus, Diana and trophies of classical arms, the finial of Ionic form, carved with relief masks of lions and satyrs, the shaped, single-edged blade, etched and gilt at the forte and engraved with a shield charged with a cross.

Dimension: L. 27.5 cm

J. H.

114   KNIFE.
Netherlands, probably Antwerp, late XVIth century.

Boxwood handle of rectangular section, carved on each side with low reliefs, representing on one side, Abraham about to sacrifice Isaac and Judith with the head of Holophernes and on the other with Adam and Eve and David with the head of Goliath, the sides carved with Adam digging and Eve spinning and with trophies of classical armour accompanied by explanatory texts in Flemish, the handle terminates above in an Ionic capital surmounted by a vase finial.

Shaped, single-edged blade, etched and gilt next to the handle, silver ferrule.

Dimension: L. 27.5 cm

J. H.

114   113

115 BOXWOOD FRAME WITH FOUR LABOURS OF HERCULES.
Andrea Brustolon (1662–1732).

Entirely carved from one single piece of boxwood with foliated scrolls and acanthus leaves and Hercules killing the Nemean lion, the hydra of Lerna, Cerberus (the three-headed monster) and the Ceryneian hind. In the centre has been left an oval opening which probably contained a miniature.

Dimensions: 20.5 × 17.5 cm

Brustolon was perhaps the only Italian carver of the late Baroque period capable of attaining a standard of craftsmanship comparable with that of his Northern (i.e. German) colleagues: in fact he came from the upper part of the Veneto where a tradition of this sort of manual dexterity existed. Although this frame is not signed or documented, it can be attributed to the master himself not only from the point of view of sheer quality, but also through an analysis of the style. Comparisons can be made with details of some of the furnishings made for the Venier di San Vio family (today in the Ca' Rezzonico Museum, Venice)[1], especially with a group showing Hercules between the Hydra and Cerberus which is fully signed and for which there is a drawing in the Museo Civico of Belluno. Another drawing by Brustolon in the same Museum – a design for a frame with an intricate assemblage of putti and allegorical animals – is very similar to our frame. A still closer example – although of much larger size and importance – is the reliquary of S. Innocenza, a masterpiece of carving in boxwood and ebony which was made for the Cathedral of Feltre in 1715 and for which the original dated design survives. This work, which is now in the Museum für Kunst und Gewerbe in Hamburg, displays the same combination of naturalistic foliated motifs and human bodies, all treated with a supreme mastery of the medium.

1.   The Venier furnishings (which have not yet been dated properly, although they may have been made about 1695 before Brustolon left Venice and returned to his home town of Belluno, whilst continuing to work there for some of his Venetian clients) is illustrated in the monograph by G. Biasuz and M. G. Buttignon, *Andrea Brustolon,* Padua, 1969, pp. 53–54. The drawing to which we refer is reproduced on p. 60 of the same book and both the S. Innocenza reliquiary and the drawing for it are on pages 90 and 91. The above-mentioned authors quote Brustolon's inscription on this last drawing to the effect that the ornaments were made without disturbing each other: *il tutto senza confusione,* something which we also see in this frame.

A. G.-P.

FURNITURE

116 CABINET.
Innsbruck, second half of XVIth century.

Rectangular, with fall front, the whole of the exterior veneered with *trompe l'oeil* intarsia in various woods, showing ruined classical buildings with large perspective volutes in the foreground, the top with musical instruments within a border of architectural volutes interspersed with laurel leaves. The interior of the fall front set with an oval plaque of engraved bone against a horn background showing the Suicide of Lucretia within a border inlaid with hop leaves and fruit. The interior contains a nest of eight drawers surrounding a central cupboard, inlaid with engraved bone against an ebony ground, with a hunting scene, birds and animals and, in the centre, Orpheus. Several of the engraved bone plaques are based on designs by German printmakers active in Nuremberg in the 1540s. Lucretia is based on *The Suicide of Lucretia* by Georg Pencz (Landau 87) and a number of the animals on the small drawers are taken from *Orpheus and the Animals* by Virgil Solis (O'dell-Franke D. 66).

Original etched and gilt iron carrying handles and lockplate.

Dimensions: 35.3 × 23 × 25 cm

Cabinets of this type were made in Augsburg, in Innsbruck and in Spain by artists who went from Augsburg to work for Philip II in the Escorial. The introduction of other materials for the decoration of the interior of this cabinet is quite exceptional. For these intarsia cabinets, see L. Müller, *Der Wrangel Schrank und die verwandten süddeutschen Intarsienmöbel des 16 Jahrhunderts,* Berlin, 1956.

J. H.

117 CABINET.
Iacobo Fiamengo (?) and Giovanni Battista de Curtis.
Naples, end of the XVIth century.

Palisander, ebony and ivory veneer.

Of rectangular form with two doors, the lock on the right is missing and the circular ivory plaque has been repaired. On these doors there are two engraved ivory panels showing scenes on battlefields enclosed by mannerist frames with caryatids, garlands and recumbent deities, supported by winged figures. On the front surrounding the centre panels are medallions and square panels with battle scenes. At the top on all sides are twelve small medallions showing Caesars. On the sides other panels show the twelve months of the year and in the centre, events from the early history of Rome. On the inner surface of the doors, two complex mannerist aedicules decorated with engraved ivory panels and turned ivory vases, enclose two panels, which continue the early history of Rome, as do the square panels in the corners. Romulus features as hero in these compositions which are based on designs by G. B. Fontana (cf. B. XVI, 227, 24–50).
  The central section is divided by six engraved ivory Corinthian columns showing the Virtues. Between them three niches enclosing engraved ivory panels with further scenes from the life of Romulus (the central scene is repeated in other pieces of furniture, as will be stated below, and like the others it has an inscription which reads *Victor roman rediens acronis spolia in capitolio iovi/Feretrio A sacra quercu suspendit romulus*, B. 38). On the upper storey, two more scenes from the life of Romulus and others showing Musica and another deity.
  On the base are other rectangular ivory panels which continue the story of Romulus. All these elements, including the columns, can be removed to disclose drawers and secret receptacles. The central door contains a miniature cabinet with engraved ivory panels with mythological subjects which can be entirely removed from the interior. The sides of the remaining void can be removed to disclose still more drawers with mythological engravings on the ivory fronts. The cabinet is also fitted with a detachable panel, the top of which covers a space containing a number of receptacles and drawers. The back of the cabinet is lined with palisander and ivory.

  Dimensions: 97 × 105 × 52 cm

In 1975 an article was published about a cabinet which was then in the art market and is today in the Museum für Kunst und Gewerbe in Hamburg[1].

This remarkable piece of furniture has an engraved ivory panel identical to the one in the main aperture of no. 117. It not only bears the same inscription concerning Romulus but is more or less identical in design (this one is rectangular, the one in Hamburg arched at the top). It is also signed "Io: Battista de Curtis faciebat". The Hamburg cabinet contains a *mappa mundi* likewise engraved on ivory, which is signed "Iannuarius picicato fecit Anno 1597". The article pointed out the stylistic similarity of the Hamburg cabinet to two other remarkable pieces which are in the Museo di San Martino, Naples, presumably given to the Duke of Alba. In a later article[2] these pieces were studied in greater detail and it was possible to establish various other facts. Whilst nothing is known about Picicato, Giovanni Battista de Curtis signed a contract in Naples with a *scrittorista* (or cabinet maker) called Iacobo Fiamengo on 31st July, 1596. In this document De Curtis is said to be Neapolitan and is defined as an *intagliatore* or engraver. Some other contracts in the State Archives of Naples show that Iacobo Fiamengo also worked with other ivory engravers like Iacobo Manganiello from Naples (in 1594), Petrus Pax Alemanus (German) in 1596. In the same year Jacobo Fiamengo also had another German, Corrado Mayer as an apprentice, and in 1602 an Italian, the twelve-year-old Natale Cassese. In one of these documents Iacobo is called *scrittorista d'avorio*, which probably means that he was able to work on ivory, although not with the accuracy that we see in our piece and in the other examples that can be attributed to De Curtis since he needed to use all the specialised craftsmen to ornament his furniture. The collaboration with De Curtis was not only limited to the occasion already mentioned because we know of at least one other contract agreed between them on the 10th January, 1596. Nothing of course confirms the attribution of any of these works to Iacabo Fiamengo, because none of them is signed, nor do the quoted documents specifically mention them, but he is very possibly their author: all this furniture shows a consummate mastery of the art of the cabinet-maker, a mastery which no Italian craftsman was ever able to achieve. On the other hand, the work of De Curtis is clearly established by the signed panel in the Hamburg Cabinet which, as it has been said, is identical to ours. The same composition also appears in another cabinet in the Galleria Doria Pamphilj in Rome, which was altered in the XVIIIth century but without damaging the engraved ivory panels. This panel is, like ours, of rectangular shape. All these pieces of furniture are obviously made in the same workshop, as they show similar technical and stylistic peculiarities. The same can be said of two more pieces, a cabinet in a Madrid private collection (still unpublished) and one in the Philadelphia Museum of Art. The connection with Naples is further established by the presence in some of these pieces of views of that city. The two cabinets in the Museo di San Martino may also be by the same hand but they are dated 1619 and 1623, which is almost a quarter of a century later than the date of the piece in Hamburg and, probably, of ours. It is possible, however, that the same craftsmen kept on working in Naples for that length of time.

Not much more is known about Giovanni Battista de Curtis except that he was probably a member of a family of craftsmen from a town near Naples, Cava dei Tirreni, where they were active in about 1570[3].

In a recent article, D. Alfter[4], who was unaware of both previous publications, again illustrated the Hamburg piece: he was able to establish that, like ours, some of the ivory panels were derived from a series of engravings by G. B. Fontana. These cabinets contain direct political references to the Hapsburg family in power not only in Austria but also in Spain and Naples (the San Martino cabinet is a glorification of the Spanish kings and one of them contains a representation of the Battle of Lepanto and of its hero, Don Juan of Austria).

D. Alfter believes that the story of Romulus, which is often seen in these pieces of furniture, including no. 117, is a direct allusion to Philip II of Spain (and Naples) as mediator between the divine realm and human destiny, and as the founder of a new "monarchia universalis". Although this is not certain it is a plausible and a fascinating hypothesis.

1.   A. González-Palacios in *Bolaffi-Arte*, November, 1975, issue 54, p. 13.
2.   A. González-Palacios, "Giovanni Battista De Curtis, Iacobo Fiamengo e lo stipo manierista napoletano", *Antologia di Belle Arti,* II, May, 1978, issue 6, pp. 136–148.
3.   G. Filangieri, *Documenti per la storia, le arti e le industrie delle provincie napoletane*, Naples, 1891, Vol. V, p. 156.
4.   D. Alfter, "Ein neapolitanischer Kabinettschrank des Giacomo Fiammingo (?) und Giovanni Battista De Curtis", *Pantheon*, XXXVII, April/June 1979, p. 135–141.

A. G.-P.

118   CABINET.
Florence, c. 1615.

Palisander wood, ebony and mosaics of *pietra dura*.

This cabinet, which is in the form of a rectangle with the front *à abattant* is completely veneered with palisander wood and ebony, round a number of *commessi di pietra dura* or mosaic panels. Inside, a central panel with an oval plaque and a landscape on a lapis-lazuli ground is framed with flowers on a dark ground of *paragone* marble opening like a small door. The inner compartment is lined with a panel of geometrical design on a lapis-lazuli ground; it contains four small drawers with *verde di Corsica* and jasper fronts and a fifth drawer showing some ducks bathing; all these drawers have *guilloché* ebony surrounds. Above the central oval plaque there are five panels with an alabaster ground decorated with animals (these conceal drawers). The lower part has a similar arrangement, while the sides contain three vertical drawers whose fronts are decorated with flowers on an alabaster ground; the middle section contains eight small and two large drawers whose fronts have panels of agate on a dark ground inlaid with flowers. The inside of the *abattant* is composed of two round panels with birds around an octagonal panel with a bouquet of flowers. The outside of this sloping front more or less repeats the same decoration, and in both cases the palisander borders are inlaid with small plaques of *pietra dura* work with geometrical designs. The top has two vertical panels with flowers and a central horizontal one with a trellis of flowers. The sides each have an oval panel decorated with a bouquet of lilies and other flowers, surrounded by ornamentation in the auricular style, all in *pietra dura* on a dark ground of *paragone* marble. The back of the cabinet is veneered with reddish palisander wood, inlaid in the form of a cross. The palisander veneer forms frames, some of which are delicately engraved (on the outside) or inlaid with fine lines of pewter.

Dimensions: 61 × 97 × 41 cm

This appears to be one of the earliest cabinets made in Florence in what was then called the *Galleria dei Lavori in Pietre Dure*, housed in the Uffizi. The various decorative motifs that figure on this distinguished piece of furniture can be related to the work of Jacopo Ligozzi, who worked in the *Galleria* for many years and whose masterpieces, the octagonal table made for Ferdinand II and Vittoria della Rovere, and the table top decorated with the View of Leghorn, are still in Florence. This cabinet is probably the work of one of the craftsmen of German origin who worked in the employ of the Medici throughout the whole century. The Germanic character of the construction recalls for instance the cabinet now in the Kunsthistorisches Museum in Vienna with *pietra dura* panels by the Castrucci, which was made in Prague about 1620[1] for the Emperor Rudolf II. On the other hand the earliest cabinet made in Florence and still in that city is the one identified some years ago in the Palazzo Vecchio. It belonged to Don Lorenzo de' Medici and is mentioned in the inventory of his possessions at the Villa della Petraia made after his death in 1649[2]. Subsequent research has shown convincingly that the central panel of Don Lorenzo's *stipo* or cabinet, which is decorated with a view of his villa on an alabaster ground, is probably after a design by Giovanni Bilivert, and that it most probably dates from the period 1615–20[3]. Like Don Lorenzo's, the present cabinet also has a central panel with a lapis-lazuli and alabaster ground and a view of a castle near a bridge. The employment of such a ground for these *commessi di pietre dure* is characteristic of the first part of the XVIIth century in Florence. After the reign of Ferdinand II it was abandoned in favour of the black *paragone* marble ground which continued to be used until the middle of the XVIIIth century. In the present cabinet, as in most early XVIIth century examples, both kinds of ground are employed. It has a series of small panels, also on an alabaster ground, decorated with flowers and animals. These compositions are close in style to the work of artists like Filippo Napoletano, Bernardino Poccetti, and later the young Stefano della Bella. As is known, the production of a piece of cabinet work in the Medici workshops was the result of the combined efforts of various artists. In the present instance it is possible that the central panel may have been designed, like the one made for Don Lorenzo, by Bilivert, who received payments in 1615 for a series of drawings of the various Grand-ducal villas that were to be used for *pietra dura* panels (this document, which is dated 15th May, 1615 speaks of payment to the artist ". . . for having sent a young man in my employ to all the villas to make coloured watercolour drawings of them to be used in the design of *pietra dura* work for little tables or whatever other designs His Highness might have in mind . . .")[4]

The use of stones left in their natural state, without figurative designs, as occurs on some of the fronts of the interior drawers, also points to an early stage in the history of the manufacture of *pietre dure*; this was a practice that was not characteristic of work made in Rome, where cabinets of this sort were made throughout the XVIIth century. In Florence a tendency to employ stones with picturesque designs prevailed.

As has already been said, all the other panels of this cabinet are close to the work of Jacopo Ligozzi at a late stage of his activity in Florence (he died in 1627). Examples are the *prie-dieu* at the Palazzo Pitti which incidentally resembles this piece in terms of cabinet work, with a similarly naturalistic use of flowers[5]; another table in the Palazzo Pitti and related pieces in Munich and elsewhere[6] which show birds playing with flowers; and again in the Palazzo Pitti, the chessboard designed by him in 1619, where he employed the same naturalistic ornament[7]. The complicated design of the middle panel on the top is also close to some of Ligozzi's creations, and the same may also be said of the bouquets of flowers on the sides of the cabinet, and on the inside and outside of the *abattant*.

Considered as a piece of furniture, this cabinet would seem to be earlier than the one that belonged to Don Lorenzo, suggesting a date of about 1615. Some of the panels may even be a little earlier than this as they are very close to the style of Poccetti, who died in 1612. No evidence has emerged so far as to the provenance of this piece, but it was in all probability made either for one of the members of the Grand-ducal family, or else as a present for some foreign sovereign.

1. The *tischler* or cabinet-maker of this piece is unknown: see H. Kreisel, *Die Kunst des deutschen Möbels*, Munich, 1968, Vol. I, fig. 371.

2. A. González-Palacios, "Un quadro e un mobile di Don Lorenzo de' Medici", in *Antologia di Belle Arti*, I, 1977, p. 301.

3. A. M. Giusti, *La Capella dei Principi e le Pietre Dure a Firenze*, Milan, 1979, fig. 142–43, Catalogue no. 101, p. 291.

4. See note 3.

5. According to the researches of K. Aschengreen Piacenti, "Osservazioni intorno a un inginocchiatoio al Museo degli Argenti", in *Antichità Viva*, 1974, no. 3, fig. 1, this is to be dated to the years 1621–24.

6. This is the table in the Palazzo Pitti, reproduced in the catalogue referred to above, note 3, fig. 17, no. 12. Another table of the same period and stylistically close to this was on the art market in Rome some years ago (its dimensions are 88×118 cm, photo. Arte Fotografica, neg. no. 41787). Another similar table is in the Museo del Prado (black *paragone* ground, a parrot in the centre with a garland and various bouquets of flowers), while a fourth example is in the Bayerisches Nationalmuseum in Munich, with a *paragone* ground and a central octagonal panel containing various flowers and a snail. Two panels with vases of flowers similar in design to the one on the *prie-dieu* designed by Ligozzi have been inserted into an early XIXth century *bas d'armoire* in the Royal Collection, at Marlborough House. The two side panels on a famous commode by Weisweiler at Buckingham Palace should also be attributed to Ligozzi; for a colour reproduction, see the study of the collection edited by J. Harris, G. de Bellaigue and O. Millar, London, 1968, p. 174.

7. See the article referred to above, note 5.

A. G.-P.

119 CABINET.
Germany, 1659.

Ebony, tortoiseshell, mother of pearl, engraved ivory. Of architectural form with ornamental brackets and a *trompe-l'oeil* chessboard that simulates a gallery ending in an arch flanked with ivory bas-relief caryatids, supported by a base containing a side drawer and a pull-out writing panel; the top crowned with double volutes round a clock. Side handles in carved and gilt brass and bronze. The entire central panel opens to disclose twelve horizontal drawers and three vertical ones set behind niches containing three silver figures of Virtues (which are probably earlier and in the style of Jamnitzer). The inside of the door is veneered with an intarsia of geometrical motifs. The clock has been altered in the XIXth century.

Dimensions: 38 × 61 × 32 cm

Although obviously made in Germany, this cabinet was ordered for or presented at the marriage of two members of the Milanese aristocracy. Stylistically this piece of furniture is not difficult to date; all the elements in it point to the second quarter of the XVIIth century. Problems arise, on the other hand, about the city in which it was made. Despite the quality and sophistication of this piece, hardly any comparative examples are known. H. Kreisel, in his standard work, *Die Kunst des deutschen Möbels* (Munich, 1968), has illustrated a cabinet that has a similar decoration with ebony volutes which dates from the same period as ours. He believes that it was made either in Austria or Bohemia (Vol. 1, fig. 372). But volutes of this type and the geometrical pattern of the intarsia as it appears on our cabinet seem to be more typical of Augsburg where similar ivory plaques were also engraved. The coat-of-arms in the centre of the support is that of Count Fabio Visconti Borromeo (1637–1683) unpalming that of the Arese. On the 23rd October, 1659, he married Margherita Arese, who was the daughter of Count Bartolomeo Arese, then President of the Senate of Milan. The cabinet was almost certainly made for their marriage. (This information was kindly given by Count Franco Arese.)

This is not the only important piece of German furniture made for an Italian. The most famous is the cabinet presented to the Grand-duke of Tuscany Ferdinand II and still in the Palazzo Pitti. It may also be remembered that during the entire XVIIth century many German cabinet makers were active in various Italian capitals.

A. G.-P.

120 CABINET.
Spain (?), last quarter of the XVIIth century.

Of rectangular form, ebonised and turned wood, the doors are covered with a rich embroidery in silk and silver thread showing a floral decoration which also appears on the sides and at the top. Inside, the cabinet contains eight horizontal drawers each decorated with *verre eglomisé* panels with a floral polychrome decoration on gold ground, secured by *guilloche* frames. The central aedicule decorated in the same fashion, opens to disclose four smaller drawers. The cabinet has its original support with turned legs joined by a stretcher.

Dimensions: H. 130 cm; Cabinet alone, 57 × 85 × 42 cm

The origin of this piece of furniture poses various problems, especially regarding its geographical provenance. The *verre fixé* plaques appear to be of Netherlandish manufacture. R. J. Charleston has kindly pointed out that there is a similar piece in the Victoria and Albert Museum, and there is also a pair of cabinets, widely regarded as Flemish, with similar glass panels, which was once in the collection of Alphonse de Rothschild[1]. However, the construction of the cabinet leaves some doubt about this. It is possible that it may have been made in Spain or at least partly re-set in that country some time in the second half of the XVIIIth century.

Indeed, some examples of Spanish cabinets in the Museo de Artes Decorativas, Madrid[2], have similar supports but no glass decoration. The embroidery panels which decorate the outside of the cabinet, which make a most striking contrast of colour and technique, and which were specially made for it as the proportions show, could also be Spanish. According to Mr. Donald King they can be safely regarded as South European and dated during the second half of the XVIIth century. Contacts between Flanders and Spain were frequent, as is well known, so it seems plausible that this unique piece of furniture could have been made in Spain using glass plaques bought elsewhere. This is something which often happened, for instance, with *pietra dura* panels bought in Florence and used in pieces of furniture made in other Italian cities or in Germany, France or England.

1.   Reproduced in colour in the sale catalogue *Meubles et Objets d'Art provenant de l'Hôtel Lambert et du Chateau de Ferrières*, Sotheby Parke Bernet, Monte Carlo, 25th/26th May 1975, lot 307.
2.   Reproduced in A. Ciechanowiecki's article on "Spanish and Portuguese furniture" in *World Furniture*, edited by Helena Hayward, London, 1965, p. 103.

A. G.-P.

121   MIRROR FRAME.
Naples, 1734–1746. Attributed to Gennaro Sarao.

Tortoiseshell veneer inlaid with mother of pearl and gold *piqué et posé*.

The form with its scrolled outline is typical of the Italian Baroque style, with as yet no trace of the Rococo. At the top, between the figures of Minerva and a winged cherub, are the arms of Philip V of Spain and his second Queen, Elisabetta Farnese, surmounted by the royal crown. The sides are decorated with panels inlaid with small figures and animals, while at the base there is a chinoiserie genre scene. The two scrolled brackets, which are detachable, are also similarly decorated; the back is lined with tortoiseshell.

Dimension: H. 53 cm

Philip V, grandson of Louis XIV, became King of Spain in 1700. In 1714 he married Princess Elisabetta Farnese, the daughter of the heir to the Duchy of Parma. Their first son, Don Carlos, was sent to Italy in 1731, firstly as heir to his mother's Duchy, and secondly as *Gran Principo Eresirario* of Tuscany. In 1734 he occupied the Kingdom of Naples, and a year later was also crowned King of Sicily. The art of the *tartarugari*, or tortoiseshell inlayers, was already flourishing in Naples, and a number of dated or datable examples exist from before his arrival there. Philip V died in 1746, and the throne of Spain passed to Don Carlos's brother Ferdinand VI (son of his father's first marriage with a Piedmontese princess). Don Carlos remained in Naples as King until 1759, when Ferdinand died and he succeeded to the throne of Spain as Charles III. It is therefore clear that this mirror, which must have been a present from the King of Naples to his mother (and we know from their correspondence that he sent her many objects made in Naples, particularly snuff-boxes and pieces made in his porcelain factory at Capodimonte) dates from the period of Don Carlos's accession as King of Naples in 1734 and his father's death in 1746.

It is almost certain that this mirror frame is by Gennaro Sarao, who made a number of pieces of this kind for the royal household during Don Carlos's reign and later on. His name appears on various similar works such as the writing desk set in the Palasciano Collection, Bari, a tray in the Wernher Collection, Luton Hoo, another writing desk set in the Wallace Collection (Inv. no. XXII A. 35), a box (sold at Sotheby's, 18th March, 1967, lot 157), a larger box set on tortoises (sold at Sotheby's, 12th February, 1981, lot 29) and a small chest with various precious implements, made for Queen Sophie Magdalen of Denmark, at Rosenborg (this is not only signed but also dated 1731). Other documents relating to Sarao's work survive, and reveal that he continued to be active until about 1772. Another unpublished document in Naples shows that he also enjoyed administrative offices in the Royal household at the Royal Villa in Portici, where he lived (Archivio di Stato, Casa Reale Antica, 1160, fol. 139 *r*).

A. G.-P.

TEXTILES

1. A man and a woman kneel before a vase, which stands on a table supported by dolphin heads; by the man is an inscription, *SAT CITO*, and by the woman, *SI SAT BENE*. The surrounding ornament includes a female mask, swags of fruit, drapery and a semi-circular awning above. Unlike the other panels this one has no framed mythological scene. Perhaps it was conceived as the central panel of the ensemble, but the embroidered vertical line on the extreme left, not present in the other panels, suggests that this one may have been the first executed. The embroiderer's rendering of the design is especially crisp and assured in this panel, which may conceivably have been executed by the head of the workshop as an example to his assistants in executing the others.

122 A SET OF EMBROIDERIES.
Paris, c. 1560–1570.

ORIGINS OF THE GROTESQUE STYLE

The discovery in Rome, at the end of the XVth century, of fine and almost intact examples of ancient Roman wall and ceiling decorations had a profound and lasting effect on the European tradition of ornament. These ancient paintings and stuccoes, decorating the plaster surfaces of walls and ceilings with representations of architectural forms, statues, framed pictures, vases, garlands, animals, birds and other heterogeneous motifs assembled in a fanciful and often highly illogical manner, were described in Italian as *grottesche*. Benvenuto Cellini explains the term as follows: "They have got this name in modern times from having been found by antiquaries in certain underground caves in Rome, these caves having been in ancient times chambers, bath-houses, studies, halls and such like. The antiquaries finding them in those cavernous places – for while the ground has been raised in the course of time, these chambers have remained below, and in Rome are called grottos – hence has sprung the term grotesques."

The most important find was made in about 1493, that of parts of the celebrated Domus Aurea, Nero's Golden House, destroyed after the emperor's death in 68 A.D., and later incorporated in the foundations of the Baths of Trajan. The impact of that discovery was immediately apparent in the work of artists then in Rome, for instance, from 1494 onwards in details of Pinturicchio's decoration of the Borgia Apartments in the Vatican. But it was Raphael – among his Papal appointments was that of Conservator of Roman Antiquities – who first achieved a deeper understanding of the principles of ancient Roman decoration and who launched the grotesque style on its European career. Vasari tells us, in his life of Giovanni da Udine, who was Raphael's specialist assistant in this field: "Not long after, in digging near S. Pier ad Vincola among the ruins of the palace of Titus, they found some rooms roofed in, covered with grotesques, small figures and scenes in stucco. Giovanni and Raphael, who were taken to see them, were amazed at their beauty, freshness and excellence, which had been preserved so long; but it is not remarkable, because they had been protected from the destructive influence of the air. These grotesques, so called from being found in grottos, executed with design, variety and fancy, and with stucco ornaments traversed by delicate colours, with their light and beautiful scenes, so captivated Giovanni that he set himself to study them, and he drew them over and over again until he could do them with ease and grace . . .". The fruits of this study and collaboration between Raphael, da Udine and other assistants in the studio were the superb grotesque decorations made for two members of the Medici family, those of the Vatican Loggie (c. 1517–19) for Pope Leo X and those of the Villa Madama for Cardinal Giulio de' Medici, later Pope Clement VII. Following Raphael's death in 1520 this style, propagated by his former assistants and by other Italian artists and engravers, spread throughout Italy and to other countries of western Europe, eventually affecting not only architectural decoration but also book design, ceramics, furniture, metalwork, textiles and all branches of the applied arts.

THE GROTESQUE STYLE IN XVIth CENTURY FRANCE

It is not possible here to follow all these widening ripples, but it is appropriate to say something of the arrival of the grotesque style in France. This was largely due to Francesco Primaticcio, who had worked under Raphael's former assistant Giulio Romano on the palace decorations in Mantua from 1526 to 1532 and who had the opportunity, during his visit to Rome in 1540, to study both the ancient Roman originals of the grotesque style and the modern versions by Raphael, Giovanni da Udine and Perino del Vaga. These studies bore fruit in the decoration of the immense Galerie d'Ulysse at Fontainebleau, which included grotesques designed by Niccolò dell'Abate and Antonio Fantuzzi under Primaticcio's direction. The Galerie d'Ulysse was demolished in the XVIIIth century, but the design of one bay of the vault, dating from about 1550, is recorded in an engraving by Jacques Androuet du Cerceau; it shows pictorial subjects in frames of various shapes and sizes, surrounded by light and elegant grotesques including herms, masks, vases, draperies, animals and so on[1]. The grotesque style, having been introduced into France by Italian artists, was immediately taken up by French engravers such as du Cerceau and Etienne Delaune, whose engravings of ornament, intended as models for craftsmen, were widely distributed. Grotesque ornaments were also disseminated by printed books, for example the page-borders of the *Metamorphoses* of Ovid published at Lyon in 1557. During the third quarter of the XVIth century the grotesque style of ornament was the height of fashion in France.

It was natural that grotesques, employed initially for wall and ceiling decoration, should quickly be adopted for tapestry wall hangings – in France, as well as in Italy and Flanders. French tapestries of this type, probably woven in the Fontainebleau workshop or in that of La Trinité in Paris, were designed with particular elegance. They include a fine but fragmentary series with the monogram of Henri II and Diane de Poitiers and hence datable between 1547 and 1559; the designs have been tentatively associated with Niccolò dell'Abate or with Androuet du Cerceau. Another tapestry, less finely woven, was made for the courtier and military leader

Claude de la Châtre some time between 1566 and 1585; the design has been associated with the circle of Niccolò dell' Abate[2]. Other tapestries of similar type are recorded in the inventory of Catherine de Médicis.

The grotesque style was also employed in France for bed hangings, but for these the preferred medium was embroidery. The Louvre has an applied work valance, to hang round the roof of a four-poster bed, with a design including grotesque motifs and the monogram of Henri II and Diane de Poitiers, indicating a date between 1547 and 1559[3]. In the same technique and of about the same date is a large and very striking panel of grotesque ornament, probably a bed-head, recently acquired by the Victoria and Albert Museum; fragments of the matching valances are in the Musée des Arts Décoratif, Paris[4]. In a different technique, with stitchery of brightly coloured silk threads on a yellow satin ground, is a set of three bed valances, of which two are in the Musée des Tissus, Lyon, and the third in the Metro-politan Museum, New York; they have been dated about 1560–70 on the evidence of the costumes depicted in the New York piece[5]. Among the grotesques on these three valances are a number of small framed scenes adapted from some of Bernard Salomon's series of 178 illustrations of Ovid's *Metamorphoses*, published in Lyon by Jean de Tournes in 1557; since the embroidered scenes are reversed in relation to these woodcuts, it may be that the embroidery designer used the reversed woodcut copies by Virgil Solis, published in Frankfurt in 1563, but it has also been suggested that he may have had access to Salomon's original designs. Closely related to this set of valances, and possibly made in the same workshop, is another em-broidered valance at Waddesdon Manor[6]. Apart from surviving examples, many richly embroidered beds are recorded in French inventories of the XVIth century, for example one in the inventory of Gabrielle d'Estrées (d. 1599), "semé d'oyseaulx, bestions, fleurs et autres grotesques de soye de toutes couleurs".

A SET OF EIGHT FRENCH EMBROIDERIES

This set of embroideries, published here for the first time, is worked on a background of bright crimson satin, woven on a loom with eight shafts; the technique and colour of the satin are characteristic of the XVIth century. At some points on the satin it is possible to see the ink drawing provided by the designer to guide the embroiderers. The embroidery is worked with silk thread in bright tones of blue, yellow, green, brown, mauve, pink, crimson and cream. It is skilfully executed in split, stem and chain stitches, with a little laid and couched work. There is slight surface wear both in the satin background and in the embroidery (especially noticeable in flesh parts) but the colours are remarkably fresh and unfaded.

Presumably in the XIXth century, each embroidery was edged with gold braid and mounted on a separate card covered with cream satin. The sight size of the embroideries, exclusive of the mounts, is about 29 cm high by about 26 cm wide. The satin-covered cards were bound up as an album in a red velvet cover inscribed *RICAMI DEI MEDICI*. The embroideries are of fine quality and could conceivably have been made for Catherine de Médicis or some other member of the French court, but there is no internal evidence of the original owner. The motto on embroidery no. 1 is not known to have any personal significance. The little panel with a dolphin in embroidery no. 5 is too inconspicuous to suggest a connection with a French Dauphin and was probably a commonplace of grotesque design; similar dolphin panels appear in the borders of Claude de la Châtre's grotesque tapestry.

The designer of these embroideries was working in the tradition of grotesque ornament which flourished in France in the third quarter of the XVIth century. He almost certainly knew the ceiling decoration of the Galerie d'Ulysse at Fontainebleau, or at least the du Cerceau engraving of it; many of his motifs – the semi-circular ornaments at the top of nos. 1 to 3, the strangely shaped shields in no. 6, and many others – are to be found there. His designs also have much in common with those of the French grotesque tapestries mentioned above. But they are most nearly related to those of other French embroideries and especially to the set of bed valances in Lyon and New York. Among many other features in common, these embroideries, like those, include variously shaped frames displaying scenes from the *Metamorphoses* of Ovid adapted, in reverse, from Bernard Salomon's illustrations, published in Lyon in 1557. The scenes of Apollo and Daphne and of Pyramus and Thisbe occur in both sets, and with the same variations from the Salomon originals.

It seems almost certain that the present set of embroideries was designed by the same hand as the set in Lyon and New York and, furthermore, that it was executed in the same embroidery workshop. The technique of the work and colours of the silk threads are almost identical and in both sets the plasticity of the motifs is emphasised by a choice of colours which produces an effect of strong light falling from the left. If, as has been suggested, the designer had access to Salomon's original drawings, then both he and the embroidery workshop may have been located in Lyon, but this is far from certain. A location in Paris, or perhaps at Fontainebleau, seems equally possible. As for the date of the present set, it is likely to have been later than the publication of the Salomon illustrations in 1557 and was presumably more or less contemporary with the Lyon-New York set, about 1560–70.

The original purpose of the present set is not known, but since the comparable embroideries were all bed hangings, it seems likely that these were intended for the same use. It was not unusual for XVIth century bed hangings to be designed as a series of approximately square panels and the present set are of the right height for bed valances. These embroideries would, it is true, produce a somewhat restless and unsatisfactory effect if they were simply aligned edge to edge, but it is quite possible that they were meant to be separated by other panels of plain or damask silk, or cloth of gold.

Whatever their original purpose may have been, these are rare and important examples of French design and of French embroidery from the time of Charles IX and his mother Catherine de Médicis. One cannot but admire the generous fertility of invention which packs each of these little panels, less than a foot square, with a host of ingenious and fanciful forms and makes of the whole set a compact treasury of grotesque ornament.

Dimensions: Each c. 29×26 cm

1.   Anthony Blunt, *Art and Architecture in France 1500–1700*, 1953, pl. 44 (A).
2.   Paris, Mobilier National, *Le Seizième Siècle Européen: Tapisseries,* 1965–66, nos. 12, 13.
3.   Illustrated by Monique Toury-King in *Needlework, an illustrated history* (edited by Harriet Bridgeman and Elizabeth Drury), 1978, p. 87.
4.   Marie Schuette and Sigrid Müller-Christensen, *The Art of Embroidery*, 1964, fig. 365.
5.   Schuette and Müller-Christensen, *op. cit.,* fig. 366, 368; Edith A. Standen, "A Picture for Every Story", in *Bulletin of the Metropolitan Museum of Art*, XV, 1957, pp. 165–175.
6.   Illustrated by Monique Toury-King, *op. cit.,* p. 90.

2. The framed subject is unidentified and does not appear to be based on any of the Salomon *Metamorphoses* illustrations. At the sides a woman and a warrior are seated on chairs beneath rectangular canopies, with dogs in front of them. The surrounding ornament includes vases, bird cages draperies, jewels and tassels, with a semi-circular awning above.

3. The framed subject, adapted, in reverse, from Salomon, is Apollo pursuing Daphne, who is changed into a laurel (*Metamorphoses*, Book I). Below, a man and a woman stand on either side of a vase sheltered by a circular canopy. The surrounding ornament includes male and female herms, sphinxes, plant pots, draperies and strings of beads, with two decorated semi-circles above.

4. The framed subject may be Venus, with Cupid, mourning the death of Adonis, but is quite different from Salomon's version of that subject. There is a smaller framed compartment with a pair of swans, below. At the sides stand a warrior and a woman. The surrounding ornament includes a laughing mask, belts, a vase, strings of beads, birds, a circular canopy and draperies.

5. The framed subject, adapted, in reverse, from Salomon, is Thisbe finding the body of Pyramus and committing suicide by falling on his sword (*Metamorphoses*, Book IV). Smaller framed compartments show a reclining nude figure, a scene of ritual at a classical altar, a dolphin and water birds. At the sides stand a pair of warriors with banners. The surrounding ornament includes monsters, birds, ox skulls, vases, wreaths and garlands.

6. The framed subject is Narcissus admiring his reflection in the pool (*Metamorphoses*, Book III); in this case the design is not based on Salomon's version, but seems to be adapted, without reversal, from a woodcut in the French translation of the first three books of the *Metamorphoses*, published by Guillaume Roville in Lyon in 1556. At the sides are a warrior and a woman, holding sceptres and seated on stools beneath rectangular canopies. The surrounding ornament includes swans, a female mask, eccentrically shaped shields, a decorated circle and flying putti.

7. The principal framed subject, adapted from Salomon and reversed, is Cyparrus turned into a cypress tree (*Metamorphoses*, Book X). A smaller framed compartment shows a standing woman. At the sides are two nude women and male and female negro herms. The surrounding ornament includes dogs, a mask, a hexagonal canopy and garlands of leaves.

8. The principal framed subject, adapted from Salomon and partially reversed is Battus turned into a stone (*Metamorphoses*, Book II). Another framed compartment shows a woman, possibly Lucretia, stabbing herself. At the sides, a woman and a man before classical altars, with garlanded hexagonal canopies above. The surrounding ornament includes winged insects and vases beneath parasol-like canopies.

123 A SILK TENT-HANGING FROM THE SIEGE OF VIENNA, 1683.
Morocco, XVIIth century.

Dimensions: 208 × 497 cm

For much of the XVIth and XVIIth centuries the military might of Ottoman Turkey was poised to strike into the heart of Christian Europe – a threat which was not finally averted until the raising of the siege of Vienna in 1683. The whole of Europe, and above all the Imperial and Polish forces who were immediately engaged, were keenly aware of the historically crucial nature of the struggle and it is therefore not surprising that the captured military booty of 1683 and subsequent campaigns was carefully preserved and revered by the victors as a symbol of their supreme achievement. Thus we may still see in the countries primarily concerned – and particularly in the museums of Vienna and Cracow – hoards of captured Turkish weapons, Turkish military standards and even the richly decorated tents of the Turkish commanders. The silk textile which concerns us here is said to have formed one wall of such a tent; a second identical panel from the same tent is stated to be in the collection of the Royal Castle of Wawel in Cracow. Until 1979 the textile remained in the family of Prince John Oginski, Palatine of Polóck, Field-Hetman of the Grand Duchy of Lithuania, who died in Cracow on 25th February, 1684 as a result of wounds suffered in the fighting around Vienna in September 1683.

It was usual for the interior of these rich Turkish tents to be decorated with a design of arches and sinuous stems of flowering plants, giving the occupants of the tent a pleasing illusion of being in an open pavilion or kiosk in the midst of a flower garden. This ornament was generally carried out in appliqué embroidery of brightly coloured cotton cloths. Rather similar in conception and design are a number of XVIIth century Turkish hangings for walls or tents, which are not embroidered but finely woven in silk and gold or silver thread. These, too, have designs of arches and a lavish display of flowers, almost Baroque in feeling; from the apex of each arch a mosque lamp is suspended. Specimens of these silk hangings are preserved, for example, at Dresden[1], in Sweden[2] and elsewhere.

The hanging which concerns us here is certainly related to the Turkish hangings just described. It, too, is woven with gold or silver thread and with silk threads in brilliant hues – red, green, yellow, cream, black and violet. It, too, has a design of arches, seven in all, alternately green and red, each with a mosque lamp suspended by a chain. But the conception and treatment of the design is simpler and more austere. Straight lines and geometrical forms predominate – octagons, stars, lattice and interlace patterns, rosettes. The flowers are few and severely stylised. The design evokes a suggestion, not of a garden kiosk, but of a building faced with patterned tilework. Technically, also, the hanging differs from the Turkish specimens; it was produced by skilful craftsmen, but using a simpler and less sophisticated loom than that of their Turkish colleagues.

It has previously been suggested that the present textile was woven in Syria (Sotheby's catalogue, 15th October 1980, lot 7), but there seems to be no evidence for this. The ornament and technique seem rather to be descended from the medieval, western Mediterranean tradition of Hispano-Moresque weaving. A number of smaller pieces of silk-weaving in the Victoria and Albert Museum, closely related to this hanging, are known to have come from Tunisia and Morocco; the Moroccan pieces, in particular, show characteristics which are virtually identical to those of the hanging. It is curious, but not really surprising, to find that a Moroccan textile was used as part of a tent at the siege of Vienna in 1683 and we need have no hesitation in identifying this piece as a very rare and outstanding example of XVIIth century silk-weaving from Morocco.

The hanging is made up of six pieces, each woven separately with a different section of the pattern, and then sewn together to form the complete design. In the completed hanging the warp threads of the pieces run lengthwise and the weft threads vertically; the individual pieces measure up to 180 m in length (warpwise) and about 1.11 m across. At the top and bottom of the hanging are broad warp stripes of various colours, alternating with narrow stripes with small geometrical patterns of warp floats. The main pattern is produced by brocaded wefts, woven on the technique known as weft-faced compound tabby, with the main warp threads working in pairs and the binding warp threads singly. The silk threads used for warp and weft have no marked twist; the metal thread consists of metal strip very sparingly wound in the 'S' direction on a thread of cream silk. Apart from some local wear and weakness, the condition of the textile is remarkably good and, except for tarnishing of the metal strip, the colours remain absolutely fresh.

1. Ernst Flemming, *An Encyclopaedia of Textiles*, n.d., pl. 300, 301.
2. Agnes Geijer, *Oriental Textiles in Sweden*, 1951, pl. 35.

D. K.

VARIA

124 A PAIR OF DRAUGHTSMEN WITH PORTRAITS OF THE
EMPEROR CHARLES V AND OF DUKE LUDWIG
Germany, early XVIth century.

Turned wood with the profiles moulded in *pastiglia*.

Charles V in profile to the right wearing a beret, shirt gown and the chain
of the Order of the Golden Fleece, with an inscription in white paint round
the raised rim *KAROLVS DEVGRACIA. CACSER* (sic).
  Duke Ludwig in profile to the left, bearded and wearing a coat with a deep
fur collar, with a chain round his neck. Similarly inscribed *DVX.
LVDOICVS. INFERIORIS.*

  Diameter: 5.2 cm each

For a group of twenty-four draughtsmen from the same workshop – and
perhaps the same hand – see examples in the collections of Albert Figdor[1]
and Adalbert von Lanna[2]. Together these total thirty-one pieces, so if a set
consisted of thirty-two (as in today's game) only one remains to be accounted
for. Another complete set from the same workshop was in the Spitzer
Collection[3].

1. Paul Cassirer, Berlin, September, 1930.
2. Rudolph Lepke, Berlin, 21st–28th March, 1911 (2nd sale), lots 29 and 65a-d.
3. Spitzer Collection, nos. 2191–2222.

  For details of various games played with draughts at this period see H. J. R. Murray,
  A History of Board-Games other than Chess, Oxford, 1952, chapter 4.

Illustration enlarged   R. F.

125   A ROOT WOOD DOUBLE CUP.
      Germany, late XVIth century.

The circular bowls turned above the naturally moulded bases, on vase-shaped
stems carved with seeds, the circular supports resembling the underside of
the bowls, the foot mounts with serrated borders above reeding, the lips
engraved with portrait medallions interrupted by panels of flowering leafage
inhabited by animals and birds.

Dimension: H. 34.6 cm

A similar example, but a single cup only, made for the Geizkofler family in
1583, was exhibited in Augsburg. The Geizkofler wedding took place in
1583 in Innsbruck. The cup bears the Augsburg hallmark and the maker's
mark of Abraham Pfleger (Rosenberg, Vol. III, no. 380).
    The present cup has mouldings and balusters in the wood identical with
the Geizkofler cup and may have come from the same workshop as the
example now belonging to the Städtische Kunstsammlungen, Augsburg.

1.   Exhibition catalogue, *Welt im Umbrech*, Vol. II, no. 739, illustration p. 359.

J. H.

126 A MOSAIC OF THE FLAGELLATION OF CHRIST.
Arminio Zuccato (died in Venice, 1606).

Signed 'Arminius Zuccatus Venetus F. MDLXXVII'. The mosaic derives from an *Ecce Homo* by Quintin Matsys which is *ab antiquo* in the Doge's Palace, Venice[1].

Dimensions: 97×78 cm

Arminio Zuccato, son of Valerio, worked at S. Pietro in Castello (perhaps after designs by Tintoretto) in 1570, and at S. Silvestro and S. Polo in 1588. *A Flight into Egypt* dated 1580 existed in a *palazzo* in Venice, while the Museo Correr possesses a *Crucifixion* signed 'Arminius Zuccato', and the Museum in Treviso has a fine panel by him after a composition of Bassano's. He also produced a mosaic of *San Geminiano* for St. Mark's, dated 1579.

Vasari attributes the rebirth of the art of mosaic in Venice to the greatest painter of the age, Titian, who, he felt, brought the art to extraordinary heights. Describing the *Last Judgement* in St. Mark's, Vasari pays the mosaics the highest compliment, saying that they "seem to be fashioned in oil colours with the brush". Some of the portraits appear to him "not so much painting as illumination" even though they are of stone. It was therefore the imitation of one material in another that earned the respect and admiration of the founder of art history; he saw it as a kind of painting for eternity. The greatest mosaic workers in Venice during that period were Valerio Zuccato and his brother Francesco, the sons of Sebastiano, who had been one of Titian's teachers, and from whose hand a single work is known – a *St. Sebastian* in the Museo Correr. It is relevant to mention here Vasari's comment at the end of his *Life* of Titian, about the relationship the latter enjoyed with the Zuccatos:

ARM
NIV
ZVE
TVI
VEN
FVI
F
M·C
LXX
VII

"But here I must not omit to say that a kind of painting which is almost discontinued in every other place, namely, mosaic, is kept alive by the most Serene Senate of Venice. Of this the benign and as it were principal reason has been Tiziano, who, so far as it has lain in him has always taken pains that it should be practised in Venice, and has caused honourable salaries to be given to those who have worked at it. Wherefore various works have been executed in the Church of S. Marco, all the old works have been almost renewed, and this sort of painting has been carried to such a height of excellence as is possible, and to a different condition from that in which it was in Florence and Rome at the time of Giotto, Alesso Baldovinetti, the Ghirlandajo family, and the miniaturist Gherardo. And all that has been done in Venice has come from the design of Tiziano and other excellent painters, who have made drawings and coloured cartoons to the end that the works might be carried to such perfection as may be seen in those of the portico of S. Marco, where in a very beautiful niche there is a Judgement of Solomon so lovely, that in truth it would not be possible to do more with colours. In the same place is the genealogical tree of Our Lady by the hand of Lodovico Rosso, all full of Sibyls and Prophets executed in a delicate manner and put together very well, with a relief that is passing good. But none have worked better in this art in our times than Valerio and Vincenzio Zuccherini (Vasari's mistake for Zuccati) of Treviso, by whose hands are stories many and various that may be seen in S. Marco, and in particular that of the Apocalypse, wherein around the Throne of God are the Four Evangelists in the form of animals, the Seven Candlesticks, and many other things executed so well, that, looking at them from below, they appear as if done in oil-colours with the brush; besides that there may be seen in their hands and about them little pictures full of figures executed with the greatest diligence, insomuch that they have the appearance not of paintings only, but of miniatures, and yet they are made of stones joined together. There are also many portraits; the Emperor Charles V, Ferdinand his brother, who succeeded him in the Empire and Maximilian, son of Ferdinand and now Emperor; likewise the head of the most illustrious Cardinal Bembo, the glory of our age, and that of the Magnificent . . . all executed with such diligence and unity, and so well harmonised in the lights, flesh-colours, tints, shadows, and every other thing, that there is nothing better to be seen, nor any more beautiful work in a similar material. And it is in truth a great pity that this most excellent of working in mosaic, with its beauty and everlasting life, is not more in use that it is, and that, by the fault of the Princes who have the power, no attention is given to it". (de Vere transl., 1912–15, Vol. IX, pp. 182–3.)

Thus we know that Titian prepared a number of magnificent designs for works executed by the Zuccatos, including one of the most solemn and at the same time least characteristic of his figures, the *St. Mark* with his arms raised, signed by the Zuccatos and dated 1543, (R. Longhi maintained that the design for this figure was the work of Lorenzo Lotto, but in this view he has not found much support.) It is in any case important to recall what the contemporary writer Francesco Sansovino had to say about this mosaic, which he described as "the most notable, noble and perfect figure that has ever been created in mosaic anywhere in the world".

Their collaboration with Titian was not limited to the St. Mark and the other mosaics in the Basilica; they also, according to Vasari, reproduced other designs by the master, including portraits of various notables, many of which have since disappeared. Among these is the portrait of Cardinal Pietro Bembo which survives in Florence, and which was most admired during the last century, but since then, has been almost completely neglected. This is signed and dated 1542[2]. Richard Lassels saw this piece during his journey to Italy in 1670, when it was in one of the rooms near the Tribuna in the Uffizi, "a picture of Cardinal Bembo is a neat Mosaick work".

1.   M. J. Friedlaender, *Die Alte Niederländische Malerei,* Vol. VII, (1929) no. 11.
2.   Reproduced in H. Tietze, *Titian,* Innsbruck, 1935, fig. 295. Small mosaic portraits of Charles V and Ferdinand I, formerly in the collection of Rudolf II in Prague, are at Schloss Ambras (see the catalogue *Die Kunstkammer,* Sammlungen Schloss Ambras, Innsbruck 1977, Catalogue nos. 342–3, figs. 30–1). A similar portrait of Charles V is in Munich (Bayerisches Nationalmuseum, Inv. no. R. 948). These mosaics reproduce designs by Titian dating from 1548.

The existence of another mosaic by the Zuccatos has been communicated by Professor Federico Zeri: *A Pastoral Scene,* after a composition by Jacopo Bassano, which was with H. Sambon in Paris in the 1950s: this may be identical with a panel showing a Biblical Scene with God appearing to a number of Shepherds inscribed "Arminius Zuccatus V.F." which has recently appeared (Christie's, *Important Sculpture and Works of Art,* 7th April, 1981, lot 9).

A. G.-P.

127   SEAL BOX.
    Austrian.
    The front and back struck with impressions from the state seal of the Emperor Ferdinand III, dated 1638.

The two faces of gold, the surround and lining of silver gilt. The top with an impression of the seal showing the enthroned Ferdinand III (reigned 1619–1637), the bottom with an impression of the Imperial arms of Ferdinand III, signed and dated *D.S.* 1638.

    Diameter: 10 cm

The lining is apparently a later addition as it obscures the two holes for the seal ribbons.

See Otto Posna, *Die Siegel der Deutschen Kaiser und Könige von Maximilian I bis Josef I*, Dresden, 1912, Vol. III, pl. 55, no. 1; for another example of the obverse, and pl. 63, no. 2 for the reverse as used by Leopold I and Josef I.

Two matrices for the reverse are known, they are almost identical; for examples of striking from the other see: Pietro Sella, *Le Bolle d'oro dell' archivo Vaticano*, Vatican, 1934, no. 31, pl. XVII and Posna, *op. cit.,* pl. 55, no. 2.

The matrix for the obverse of the present box is now in the Staatsarchiv, Vienna and that for the reverse in the Hauptstaatsarchiv, Dresden (no. 13908).

                                     J. H.

ST. JOSEPH'S RELIQUARY.
Probably by Antonio de Amicis Moretti (1611–1687), Rome, c. 1659.

Reliquary with the arms of Pope Alexander VII (Chigi, 1655–1667) in lapis-lazuli, rock crystal and silver gilt. On the lid there is a silver crown bearing two crossed palm leaves surmounted by a cross which is also in silver. In the inside of the reliquary visible through the rock crystal panels there is a silver sun with an inscription on both sides: *DE PALLIO SANCTI JOSEPH*. The object is on an ebony and lapis base which bears on the front the Chigi arms in silver, gold and enamel and there are four silver cherubs on the angles.

Dimension: H. 27.7 cm

This remarkably fine reliquary for a fragment of the cloak of St. Joseph is probably the work of the Roman goldsmith Antonio de Amicis Moretti (active 1652–87), one of the main artists in his field employed by Alexander VII and the Chigi family. In the late 1650s and 1660s he produced many pieces of elaborate jewellery for the Papal Court and some of the Cardinals. Among his other commissions were various church ornaments for the Chigi Chapel in the Cathedral in Siena (1662–66). Of particular interest here is the payment made to Moretti in June 1659 for three reliquaries, of which ours is probably one, especially as other payments seem to substantiate such a theory: on 29th May, 1659, Bonifatio Peri was paid for sets of cut rock crystals for (probably the same) three reliquaries and in April 1660 another Roman goldsmith, Giovanni Antonio Scatola (active 1656–85) was paid for enamelled coats of arms for (these?) reliquaries.

As we know that Moretti was both a jeweller and a goldsmith, the elaborate use of precious metals and hardstones points to him as the author of this Papal commission, for which he, as the chief goldsmith of the Chigi Pope, working regularly for the Reverenda Camera Apostolica, would be in any case the obvious choice. We can therefore tentatively suggest that our reliquary may be one of the three made by Moretti with the help of Scatola and Peri, and for which he was paid in 1659, which establishes the *terminus ante quem*.

L. d'U.

129 STANDING CUP.
Germany, Königsberg, mid-XVIIth century.

Amber and copper gilt, the bowl and cover composed of segments of amber
carved in low relief with animals, birds and bunches of fruit within scrollwork frames, the panels of the cover carved with interlacing strapwork,
pineapple finial, baluster foot and spreading gilt copper base, openwork
handles cast with harpies amidst scrolls.

Dimension: H. 20 cm

Lent by John Winter, Esq.   L. d'U.

273

RHINOCEROS HORN.
Rome, second half of the XVIIth century.

Rhinoceros frontal horn mounted on gilt bronze and brass.

The support is formed by three gilt bronze monopode harpies (winged and with lion feet attached to the body with foliated scrolls with a stretcher); at the top an engraved brass circle composed of volutes keeps the horn in place. This is the smaller frontal horn of a rhinoceros (it may be recalled that rhinoceros horns are composed of modified hair: some rhinoceri have only one large nasal horn while other types have both a nasal and a smaller frontal horn).

Dimension: L. 15.5 cm

Rhinoceros horns were very much collected in the *Wunderkammern*: they were either mounted like the present one or carved to make goblets or beakers. Some were totally carved and came from the Orient like the ones in the Museo degli Argenti, Florence, which date from the XVIIth century and were made in China but mounted in Europe. According to some Italian XVIIth century writers like Lorenzo Magalotti, the great Chinese lords drank from "rhinoceros horn, either smooth or worked with carving, with gold mounts enriched with jewels" (1697). Father Giovanni de Morini, a Jesuit missionary in Tonking wrote in 1665 that "the gravest mandarins of China, for greater splendour and pomp on the tables they set before their guests and at banquets do not give bowls of glass to drink from, but only cups, worked with graceful carvings, of the hard horn of this animal (the rhinoceros) esteeming that wine drunk in these will make men drink more freely and with the more enjoyment that he who drinks therefrom is free from all suspicion of poison"[1]. Rhinoceros horns of all sorts (either carved as vessels or mounted as *objets d'art* were very much in fashion in the German courts[2] but they were also collected in Italy. The Cardinal Flavio I Chigi, for instance, had six items made with this material: some were cups or vessels but there was also a *"corno della spalla di rinoceronte, sopra tartaruca di argento"* which was probably presented, like the one exhibited, in its natural state as a curiosity[3]. Stylistically the bronze support of the piece exhibited can be described as Italian, probably Roman, and dating from the second half of the XVIIth century.

1. R. Lightbown, "Oriental Art in Italy", *The Journal of the Warburg and Courtauld Institutes*, XXXII, 1969, p. 261.
2. E. von Philippovich, *Kuriositaten Antiquitäten,* Braunschweig, 1966, pp. 460–468.
3. G. Incisa della Rocchetta, "Il Museo di curiosità del Card. Flavio I Chigi", *Archivio della Società Romana di storia patria*, Vol. XX, arr. LXXXIX, fasc. I-IV, 1967, pp. 141–192, see under numbers 220, 479, 486, 589, 598, 752. This inventory of Cardinal Chigi (who had died in 1693) was made in 1706.

A. G.-P.

131 CRIB
Rome, 1696–1700.

Veneered ebony with inset lapis lazuli in bronze gilt frames, with cascades and other sculptural ornaments in bronze gilt. At the centre a niche flanked by pilasters, containing a crib in amber, its pediment surmounted by a putto with roses in full relief; the support with reversed volutes and brackets and, at the base, the inscription *AUGUSTINI CUSANI ORATORIS PONTI-FICII SYLVESTRO PNPI VALERIO MUNUS* (Gift of Agostino Cusani Papal Nuncio to the Doge Silvestro Valier).

Dimensions: H. 101 cm L. 42 cm

The Latin inscription at the foot allows us to date this portable altar between 1694 and 1700 when Silvestro Valier was Doge of Venice; it is indeed probable that it belongs precisely to 1696, the year when Agostino Cusani was appointed nuncio in Venice.[1] The presence of amber, which is rarely used by Italians, indicates probably the intervention of one or more German craftsmen. We know, moreover, that the most important cabinet-makers working at Rome in the XVIIth c. were German or Flemish, like the cele-brated Giacomo Herman, author of a famous piece given to Leopold I of Austria, now in the Kunsthistorisches Museum in Vienna. This tradition continued throughout the XVIIth century and well into the next. Some of these cabinet-makers, and Herman himself, collaborated with the chief Roman clockmakers of the period, the Campani: the cases of these clocks have architectural features very similar to this crib. This type of object was highly regarded in baroque Rome, and was often sent to foreign rulers as a gift, as recorded by Chantelou in his account of Bernini's visit to France.

1.   Moroni, *Dizionario storico-ecclesiastico,* Vol. XIX, p. 64.
2.   Other clocks by the Campani are illustrated in Lizzani, *op. cit.,* p. 86.
      See also E. Morpurgo, *Un orologio di P. T. Campani* in *La Clessidra* Dec. 1968 and the *Dizionario degli orologiai italiani* Rome 1950, by the same author, as well as the various examples illustrated in A. Simoni, *Orologi italiani* Milan 1965. (See entry 49.)

General Bibliography:
A. Gonzalez-Palacios, *Avvio allo studio dellam obilia romana* in G. Lizzani, *Il mobile romano* Milano, 1970, p. X, fig. XIX.

A. G.-P.

ORIENTALIA

---

132 CELADON DISH.
China, Longquan, late XIVth century.

A massive porcellanous dish with flattened, bracket-lobed rim and well, boldly carved in the centre with a peony spray, and in each panel of the well in front with a lotus spray, and on the back with a fungus spray, covered with a thick greyish-green slightly translucent glaze which goes right over the foot ring. On the base an unglazed red burnt ring on which the piece was fired.

Diameter: 43.5 cm

Dishes of such a large size as this were made primarily for the overseas market, especially for India and the lands of Islam, where the Longquan wares were especially admired. Great collections were made from the late XIIIth century until the early XVth century. The most famous surviving collection is that in the Topkapi Saray Muzesi in Istanbul, where there are nearly 2,000 celadons of which the greatest number are dishes. Others more easily seen are in most European museums and in many instances have been acquired in the Near East. Another dish with a carved peony spray, of earlier date is illustrated in M. Medley, *Yuan Porcelain and Stoneware*, London, 1974, pl. 71.

M. M.

133 LACQUER TRAY.
China, Ming dynasty, XVIth century.

A square tray with rounded sides and shaped corners, inlaid with mother-of-pearl. The dark brown lacquer is inlaid in the centre with a bifurcated spray of flowering prunus under a crescent moon, the panel being outlined with two narrow inlaid lines. Each rounded side is inlaid with a two-flowered chrysanthemum scroll decoration. The tray stands on four low, shaped feet, and the underside is lacquered but undecorated.

Dimension: 37.2 cm

The prunus flowering under the crescent moon is a popular motif from late Song times (XIIIth century) onward, and may be found in most media. Another interesting example in inlaid lacquer, but lacking the moon, is to be seen on the pedestal base of a rather decorative table that was shown in an exhibition of mother-of-pearl inlaid lacquers from the XIVth to the XVIIth centuries held in Tokyo National Museum in 1979[1]. The use of prunus in combination with chrysanthemum is of symbolic interest because the prunus is the harbinger of spring and an emblem of beauty, while the chrysanthemum represents autumn and has close associations with longevity. This would bestow on the owner of the piece the compliment of good looks and long life.

1.   *Chugoku no raden,* Tokyo, 1979, no. 75.

M. M.

134 BLUE AND WHITE PORCELAIN BRUSH POT (*Bitong*)
China, Jingdezhen, Kangxi period, late XVIIth century.

Cylindrical jar with straight rim, decorated round the outside in shades of underglaze cobalt blue with an emperor seated in a pavilion before a screen, with a fan holder behind him and two elegant women attendants to his left, with military guards beyond; on his right is a seated scholar with whom he is conversing, with more military guards beyond. Decorative rocks, balustrades and plants form the outside setting. The inside is glazed plain white. The base is slightly concave with a small glazed recess in the centre of a wide unglazed band.

Dimensions: H. 15.5 cm; Diameter: 18.2 cm

This is an example of the last stages of what is called the Transitional style of decoration, which began early in the XVIIth century. By the very end of the century a new style, a Kangxi style had begun to emerge, and this belongs to this period when features such as V-shaped grass elements and ornamental cloud bands which had been characteristic features of the Transitional style, had vanished from the decorator's vocabulary.

M. M.

135 JADE BIRD.
China, early XVIIIth century.

Pale greenish-white jade squatting crested bird with a millet spray in its beak, the wings lightly tinged with pale russet. The long elaborate tail, with finely marked tuft at the end, is wrapped round onto the body and overlaps one wing. The long legs are cut into the underside of the body. There is much finely incised detail.

Dimension: L. 6.8 cm

Much fine quality jade found in small pebbles is carved very economically and this is just such an example. The craftsman has cut away the minimum, and has even retained a little of the oxidised "skin" of the pebble to sharpen the effect of the design on the wings and millet spray.

Illustration enlarged   M. M.

136 SPOON.
China, XVIIIth century.

Lapis lazuli soup spoon with the handle carved at the end with a *ruyi* fungus.

Dimensions: L. 13 cm

The *ruyi* or "as you wish" fungus is associated with immortality and has been identified in the past as *Polyporus lucidus*. In nature it is rather brightly coloured, the colours varying over the surface; it is also rather hard and woody. It may grow to a considerable size, up to about 9 inches across. It is frequently used in the decorative arts to convey the idea of longevity.

M. M.

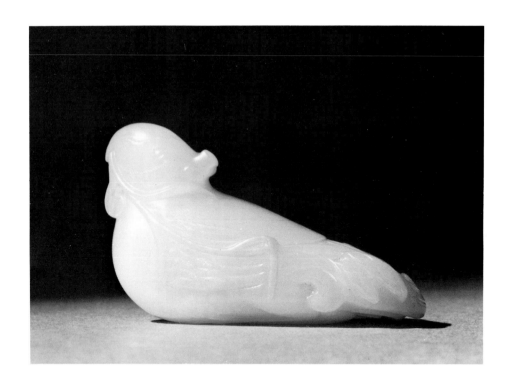

137 SPOON.
    Turkish (?), c. XVIIth century.

The shallow bowl and handle are of dark green nephrite joined with a peg and traces of resin.

    Dimensions: L. 27.7 cm; W. of bowl 7.0 cm

R. S.

138 SCABBARD MOUNTS.
Mughal, late XVIIth or XVIIIth century.

Locket and chape of dark green nephrite from the scabbard of a *khanjar*. The locket is carved in relief on either side with a flower and two buds with a lug projecting from one face. The chape has an iris on each face growing from an acanthus leaf on the outer edge whose stem is coiled at the tip.

Dimensions: (Locket) L. 3.5 cm; W. 4.8 cm
(Chape) L. 4.8 cm; W. 2.3 cm

The *khanjar* is a double-edged dagger with a slight double curve to the blade. It commonly has a jade, crystal or ivory hilt and was frequently worn as an item of court dress.

Illustration enlarged   R. S.

139 SCABBARD MOUNTS.
Mughal, late XVIIth or XVIIIth century.

The locket is of rock crystal, carved on each face with a flower and buds in low relief. A pierced lug projects from one edge. The chape, from the scabbard of a different *khanjar*, is of pale green nephrite carved on each face with an iris plant.

Dimensions: (Locket) L. 4.2 cm; W. 5.8 cm
(Chape) L. 5 cm; W. 2.5 cm (*not illustrated*)

Illustration enlarged   R. S.

140 BOWL.
Mughal, late XVIIth or early XVIIIth century.

The bowl is of thinly carved pale green nephrite and has eight lobes, slightly flared towards the rim. The two handles are formed by acanthus leaves curling outwards at the tips and lanceolate leaves are carved in low relief at the junctions of the lobes, rising from the foot ring. The underside of the foot is carved in the form of a lotus bud.

Dimensions: H. 3.8 cm; W. 9.8 cm

As in the case of Mughal architecture from the end of Jahangir's reign the foliate decoration is here derived from Renaissance Europe.

R. S.

141 POTICHE.
Mughal, early XVIIIth century.

The vessel is of green nephrite with low relief decoration. It stands on a shallow foot with a globular body and vertical neck. There are two handles in the form of buds emerging from the tops of acanthus leaves. Other serrated leaves encircle the bottom of the vessel with lotus plants arising from them and spreading over the sides. The underside of the base is carved in the form of a lotus flower. Inside the neck is an openwork filter formed by cloud scrolls radiating from a central ring.

Dimensions: H. 8.5 cm; D. 9.1 cm

R. S.

142 IMAGE OF AN ACHARYA.
Jaipur or Cambay, XVIIth or XVIIIth century.

The image of a Hindu religious teacher is carved from a pale-blue Sinhalese sapphire. He sits in a yogic posture (*dhyanasana*) with his hands raised in the conventional gestures of exposition (*vitarka* – right) and gift-bestowing (*varada* – left). He wears a *dhoti* and his head is shaven except for a top knot.

    Dimensions: H. 3 cm; W. 2 cm

This evidently represents one of the great Vaishnavite theologians, whose teachings resulted in the revival of devotion to Vishnu in Northern India during the late medieval period.

    The style of carving is characteristic of Rajasthan or Western India where Jaipur and Cambay were the leading centres of gem cutting.

Illustration enlarged   R. S.

143 KATAR.
North India, late XVIIth or early XVIIIth century.

Watered steel blade chiselled with three converging ribs and a stylised iris flower on either side. The steel handle comprises two side bars decorated with chiselled ribs and stylised iris plants and a grip of two cross-pieces joined by rings. The decorative motifs of the blade and handle are partly gilded. The sheath is covered with yellow velvet (pile worn away) and has a white metal chape, the locket being lost.

Dimensions: L. 41 cm; W. 7.5 cm (Sheath L. 23.5 cm; W. 6 cm)

The *katar* is the characteristic Indian thrusting dagger of ancient origin. It survived to the end of the Mughal period both as a weapon and as an indispensable item of court dress.

R. S.

144 KARD.
North India or Persia, late XVIIth or XVIIIth century.

Finely watered steel blade with a bone hilt. Both the blade and the tang are finely inlaid with floral arabesque scrolls in gold. The decoration on the blade incorporates the Arabic phrase, "Help is from Allah and victory near". The rear edge of the blade is finely chiselled with three ribs and a motif terminating in volutes. The wooden scabbard is covered with blue velvet trimmed with braid containing strips of silver foil. The locket and chape are of gilt bronze.

Dimensions: L. 35 cm; W. 3 cm (Sheath L. 33.5 cm; W. 4.5 cm)

The *kard* is a straight-bladed Persian knife which was also very popular in Northern India. In quality and style of decoration the best Indian examples are very closely modelled on Iranian prototypes.

R. S.

145   TUGHRA OF SULTAN MEHMET IV OF TURKEY (1648–87).
      Dated AH 1082/AD 1671.

Executed in colours and gold on paper mounted on an album page with
decorated borders.
Verso: A Turkish miniature, c. 1630–40, of a Prince picnicking with companions on a hillside.

   Dimensions: Tughra 15.5 × 26.3 cm; Miniature: 30 × 18.7 cm

The Tughra, or official insignia, of the Sultan was often placed at the head
of official documents. The finest examples were, like this one, produced by
court illuminators to the highest and most decorative standards.

M. G.

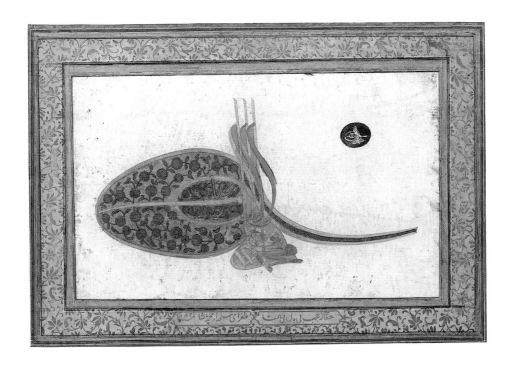

PAINTINGS

146 CIRCLE OF JOACHIM PATENIR, about 1480–1524.

The Temptation of St. Anthony

Dimensions: Oak panel, 21.5 × 34.3 cm

This is an unpublished work perhaps by Patenir himself, but more likely by one of his intimate followers, like Herri met de Bles or Cornelis Massys. It is an important example of the kind of landscape that became popular in the XVIth century. The theme of the Temptation of St. Anthony is itself a keynote to the strangeness of the view of distant lands that opens before the spectator. Small gem-like views of this kind, almost always with the pretext of a religious subject such as the Flight into Egypt, St. Christopher or St. Jerome, had a profound impact on artistic development both in the Netherlands and further south. They brought a new awareness of real landscape, even where few painters would themselves follow the lead. The Italians, with their concern for figure painting, often felt apart, as Paolo Pino, writing in 1548, puts it so charmingly:

"The Northerners show a special gift for painting landscapes because they portray the scenery of their own homeland, which offers most suitable motifs by virtue of its wildness, while we Italians live in the garden of the world, which is more delightful to behold in reality than in a painting" (*Dialogo di Pittura*, ed. Venice, 1946, p. 145). Despite this view, it was in Pino's native Venice that landscape painting really came to life in Italy, and there were strong reciprocal influences between the Veneto and the Netherlands in this genre. Works by Patinir and other contemporaries like Herri met de Bles (known universally in Italian inventories as Il Civetta, from the owl with which he signed his pictures) were highly prized in Italian and Spanish collections. Its simplicity and horizontality anticipate by a century-and-a-half the panoramas of Ruisdael and de Koninck.

C. W.

A Man and Woman admiring a Child in Masquerade Costume.

Dimensions: Canvas, 90.2 × 69.8 cm

The occasion of this exhibition is a fitting opportunity for the publication of an important newly-discovered work by Annibale Carracci, reflecting as it does the naturalistic side of his art. Enigmatic in subject-matter, it belongs stylistically with pictures of the 1580s like the *Bean Eater* in the Galleria Colonna, Rome, and other genre paintings like the *Boy drinking*, formerly in the Emmons Collection (D. Posner, *Annibale Carracci*, 1971, Vol. II, no. 9). The central figure of this new picture is the same model Annibale used in the *Boy with a Monkey* now in the Uffizi, Florence. His features are immediately recognisable, and it suggests a date of about the same period, the early 1590s, for this painting too. The pictorial technique evinces the naturalistic colouring of the years following Annibale's Venetian journey, contrasting with the bright tonality of genre subjects in Bologna of Passarottian descent.

It is more than likely that the imagery Annibale uses here, as in the *Boy with a Monkey* (where the monkey is delousing his host) had for contemporary eyes a meaning beyond the genre content, perhaps illustrating a popular saying or a philosophical commonplace. His drawings, as well as the words of Seicento historians, tell us that Annibale was incessantly drawing from subjects he found round him in daily life. The observation of this scene with a child in a mask seems, however, to represent a profounder insight into human nature than that which informs the genre scenes of Passarotti and Campi. Annibale's naturalism was undoubtedly in part a response to Post-Tridentine forces, as well as the reaction of a young painter to the artistic conventions of his day.

The group of paintings among which this work belongs shares with the artist's drawings an informality that is one of his most attractive characteristics. Absent from many of the more important commissions, particularly after the move to Rome, it is a quality that can be attributed partly to their less serious, decorative character. The young man with tousled hair, the woman laughing at her child dressed up – these are real individuals, and the directness and force of the imagery points to a recognition of this quality among the patrons for whom Annibale painted these

pictures. A later work of the same kind is the so-called *Satire on Caravaggio* in the Museo Nazionale di Capodimonte, Naples. Far from having the controversial subject-matter implied by such a title – and Annibale's naturalism was in many ways motivated by impulses similar to those of Caravaggio – the picture has been shown to be a portrait of some of the inmates of the Farnese household. The picture, which in most of the modern literature is credited to the hand of Agostino Carracci despite the earliest inventory references in the Seicento Farnese papers naming its author as Annibale, is described there as being of "Arrigo peloso, Amon nano e Pietro matto". Giovanni Incisa della Rocchetta has shown (in *"Tognina" e "Arrigo peloso"*, Strenna dei Romanisti, 1959, p. 101f.) that Arrigo and his sister Tognina were natives of the Canaries who had been given to the Farnese court as curiosities, being both of them hairy all over. The dwarf Amon was evidently a more characteristic member of such a princely collection, as perhaps also "Mad Pietro" who may well have been no more than that, rather than as has been suggested the likeness of the celebrated Bolognese naturalist Ulisse Aldrovandi.

Aldrovandi was nonetheless an important figure in the intellectual climate in which Annibale's art emerged, and we can see parallels between the aspiring objectivism of the *Historia Naturalis*, published in many volumes towards the end of the XVIth century, and the realism of Carraccesque painting. It was a kindred impulse that made Annibale, for want of a live Venus, use Lodovico's back as the model for the famous *Venus with a Satyr* now in the Uffizi, and a child of his acquaintance – who knows, perhaps his young nephew Antonio Carracci – for this charming anecdotal image.

C. W.

The *Kunstkammer* of Prince Vladislaus Sigismundus Vasa, future King Vladislaus IV of Poland.

Signed: E. Hire fecit Varsavij 1626.

Dimensions: On panel, 72.5 × 104 cm

Fourteen paintings and sketches are represented, an open album of drawings, other drawings and maps, one statue in bronze gilt, a gold medal in a jewelled frame, an inlaid box with masculine jewellery against a background of Genoese cut velvet and a rich Cabinet – all standing on a table covered with an Oriental textile.

The architecture is fantastic and does not correspond to what we know about the Royal Castle in Warsaw during the Vasa period (1587–1668).

It is interesting to note the textile covering the table, which is near-Eastern (Syrian or Persian) and is an early example of textiles appearing in paintings connected with Poland. It may exemplify booty taken by the Prince during his victory over the Turks at Chocim in 1621.

The Prince appears twice in the painting – once in the gold medal by Alessandro Abondio, which was executed in Vienna in 1624, and of which versions were known to have been given by the Prince as mementos as early as September of the same year in Brussels. His portrait also appears in the background, above the naval battle scene. The jewelled clasp of the plume is characteristic of the Polish costume of the period.

Certain of the paintings can be easily identified, for instance: David Vinckeboon's *Peasants fighting before an inn*, c. 1609 (a version in the Rijksmuseum, Amsterdam, oil on panel, 26.5 × 45 cm), J. Breughel II, *View of a village* (the closest version in a private collection in France, oil on panel, 25 × 40.5 cm; since about twenty versions of this painting are known, it is worth noting how exactly it has been represented, which makes it clear that it was copied from an original, then in Warsaw); P. P. Rubens, *The Drunken Silenus* (version in the Staatliche Museen in Berlin); J. Breughel II, *Madonna in a garland of flowers* (private collection in France, oil on panel, 43 × 33 cm).

Other paintings belong to the Northern School of the first quarter of the XVIIth century (Rubens, Spranger, Fyt, etc.).

The signature appears on an engraving by Hendrik Goudt of *Tobias and the Angel* (1608) after Elsheimer, replacing a similarly stylised one by Goudt himself.

The splendid gilt bronze example of Giambologna's *Rape of the Sabines* has not survived and its presence in Warsaw can be easily explained as a gift either from Florence or from Vienna, both courts being closely connected by family ties with that of Warsaw.

Prince Vladislaus Sigismundus Vasa (1595–1648) was the son of Sigismundus III, King of Poland and Sweden (1587–1632). His mother was the Archduchess Anne of Austria. As a boy he was elected Tsar of Russia by the boyars, but had to give up the throne as a result of the popular uprising against the Poles, which finally brought the Romanovs to power in 1613. He fought the Turks victoriously in the years 1620–21. During the years 1624–25 he went on the "grand tour" visiting Vienna, Munich, Brussels, Rome, Florence and Venice. An avid collector of paintings, he bought works of art everywhere, but particularly in the Netherlands, where the art particularly appealed to him. He sat for Rubens, and both the Prince and his entourage bought heavily from the artist. Elected King in 1632, after the death of his father, he reigned as Vladislaus IV until his death in 1648. He was succeeded by his brother John Casimir (1648–1668).

There is no question but that the present painting, which differs in its "lay-out" from the usual "cabinet d'amateur" is a photographic rendering of part of the art treasures the Prince had brought back from his "grand tour".

The Netherlandish style of this painting is slightly baffling for the hand of a French artist, who is documented as having worked in Warsaw. His paintings are hardly known, but the existence of potentially similar still-lifes is confirmed by his posthumous inventory of 1657.
writers, were decimated during the Swedish wars (1654–1660). What was left was taken to France after the abdication of John Casimir (1668), who settled in Paris and Nevers, his late wife's property. After the ex-King's death in 1672, the collections, never properly catalogued, were sold in a series of auctions in Paris.

Anonymous Loan   J. A. C.

149 FOUR ANAMORPHIC PAINTINGS.
Low Countries, c. 1770, probably by Henry Kettle.

Dimensions: On panel, each 68 × 69 cm

These paintings are examples of catoptric anamorphoses which were popular in the XVIIIth century. Diderot explained the principle behind them in his Encyclopaedia: "A cylindrical and conical mirror possesses the property of distorting things exposed to them and in consequence they can make distorted objects appear natural. In optics too there are means of drawing on paper distorted objects which, seen through this kind of mirror, appear in their natural form"[1]. These four conical anamorphoses form part of a set of ten, now dispersed, of which five are cylindrical and five conical. Made in the Low Countries, they are almost certainly the work of Henry Kettle, who specialised in this art form. (The attribution to Henry Kettle rests on a comparison of the anamorphoses of the Dogs and Boars with an almost identical anamorphic painting signed by the master)[2].

I. Venus and Adonis, after Simon Vouet.
The original of this picture is in the Hermitage and Leningrad and its oval form is here transformed into a small medallion.

II. A peasant woman riding a donkey (the picture from which this is derived is not known).

III. Animal scene with dogs and wild boars (probably after Frans Snyders)[3].

IV. Owl defending its young against an eagle (probably after Paul De Vos).

1. Diderot, *Encyclopédie ou dictionaire raisonné* . . . I, 1775, p. 405.
2. Jurgin Baltusaitis, *Anamorphic Art*, Cambridge, 1977, pp. 136–146, p. 180, note 16.
3. Exhibition Catalogue, *Anamorphoses*, Paris, Musée des Arts Decoratifs, 1976, no. 22.

L. d'U.

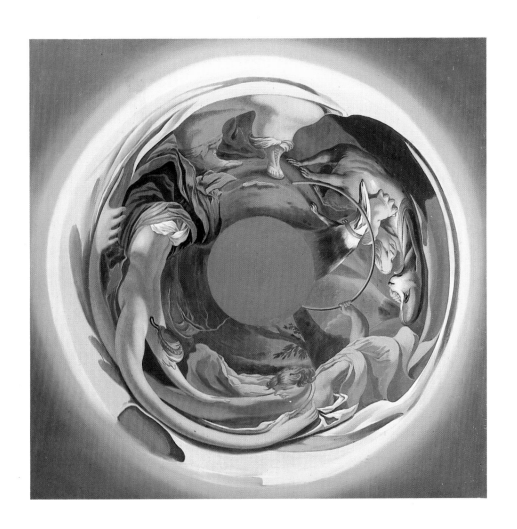

XIXth CENTURY REVIVALS

150 MEDALLION OF THE VIRGIN AND CHILD WITH A GOLDFINCH.
In the style of Benedetto da Maiano.

Ivory, uniface, within turned rim.

Dimension: 57.5 cm diam.

This medallion, not unlike a draughtsman in form, is apparently unique in
scale and choice of material, reproducing as it does the monumental *tondi*
popular for the upper zone of humanist tombs in Florence at the middle of
the Quattrocento. Precious metals or alloys such as bronze, were a more
usual material for devotional images on this scale. The finesse of the workmanship is astonishing, though it is not at the moment possible to be sure
that it is contemporary with the style of the image, or a brilliant, but later,
reproduction.

C. A.

151 A PORTRAIT RELIEF OF A MAN, POSSIBLY A PASTOR.
Germany, XIXth century.

Boxwood, round-headed plaque with strapwork motif with an incised 'D'
below.

Dimensions: H. 5.3 cm; W. 3.3 cm

This carefully carved relief portrait, showing the subject three-quarters to the
right appears to date from the period of Renaissance revival in the XIXth
century.

(*not illustrated*)   C. A.

152 CHALICE.
Paris, first half of the XIXth century.

Enamelled gold, the bowl with four applied trefoil cartouches within circular frames enclosing basse-taille polychrome enamel plaques of the Marriage of Joseph and the Virgin Mary, the Annunciation, Birth of Christ and the Circumcision (?), interspersed with four shaped panels of mauresques against a red ground each set with a large pearl and with a table-cut diamond above and below, the intervening panels also decorated with mauresques against a background of alternately translucent green and blue, the underside of the bowl with panels in translucent colours against alternately white and gold ground. Spherical knop enamelled in alternate panels of white, blue and gold, with a horizontal ring set with pairs of pin-set pearls and table-cut diamonds in cusped collets.

Rectangular stem and spreading base of Gothic design, the base divided into eight petal-shaped panels, four set with groups of four pearls and a small table-cut diamond against a pierced background, the remainder with basse-taille panels of St. Sebastian, John the Baptist, St. Peter and St. George (also carrying a pair of scales), around the base a pierced border and four pearls.

Dimension: H. 22 cm

This chalice combines decorative details drawn from ecclesiastical and secular ornament covering a period from the mid-XVth to the early XVIIth century. It appears to be one of the most sumptuous creations of the XIXth century Historicist Style.

A gold chalice of Gothic revival style was made by Froment Meurice of Paris for the Pope and shown at the Great Exhibition in 1851[1], but the most closely related object is the enamelled and jewelled silver-gilt vase in Moorish-Gothic style by Karl Wagner of Paris exhibited at the *Exposition de l'industrie française*, Paris, 1839, and acquired in that year for the Prussian Königliche Kunstkaeum, now in Berlin Kunstgewerbemuseum[2]. A replica of this vase by Rudolphi, chief of the Wagner workshop was shown in the *Exposition de l'industrie française*, Paris, 1844.

1. *The Great Exhibition of 1851, Commemorative Album*, London, 1950, fig. 130.
2. Catalogue of the exhibition, *Historismus, Kunsthandwerk und Industrie im Zeitaltar der Weltausstellungen*, Berlin, 1973, no. 46.

J. H.

ADDENDA

---

153 EMBROIDERED BED-COVER.
Spain, XVIIth century.

Yellow silk in tabby weave, embroidered with silk thread in shades of light green, light blue, pink, lilac, brown and cream silk in satin, stem and plait stitches. In the centre is a circle containing a double-headed eagle; two smaller circles, above and below, contain reduced versions of the same motif. The rest of the field is filled with floral scrolls, inhabited by parrots and other birds and by dogs pursuing deer. A border on all four sides shows similar floral scrolls with birds and, in square compartments at the corners, double-headed eagles. All round is a yellow silk fringe, with yellow silk tassels at the corners; lining of green silk in tabby weave.

Dimensions: L. 260 cm; W. 184 cm

The imperial double-headed eagle is frequently found in textiles produced for the Spanish market. The handsome design probably originated about the middle of the XVIIth century, or even slightly earlier, but a certain rusticity in the drawing, especially of the birds and animals (which recall later peasant embroideries) suggests that this version may have been executed a little later. The embroidery is skilful professional work, but probably from a provincial rather than a metropolitan workshop. The colours are absolutely fresh and unfaded.

D. K.

154 NEEDLEWORK WALL-HANGING.
Italy, mid XVIIth century.

Linen canvas, worked all over with silk thread in shades of yellow (for background, etc.), green, brown, blue, lilac, pink, red and cream, in straight, tent and knot stitches. Outlines worked with couched brown silk cord. Large-scale design of coiling stems encircled with jewelled crowns and bearing tulips, carnations, columbines, iris and other flowers. Lined with red silk damask of later date.

Dimensions: L. 275 cm; W. 190 cm

Such designs of coiling stems with a variety of blossoms were universally current in western European needlework of the XVIIth century – not least in England, where similar patterns are found on cushion covers, bed-hangings, etc. The colouring and technique of the present example, however, are indicative of Italian origin. Rather similar designs with crowns encircling the stems can be seen in Italian furnishing velvets of the middle of the XVIIth century. In the present piece four vertical panels of needlework, originally designed to be used separately as wall-hangings or bed-hangings, have been assembled subsequently to form a single large hanging.

D. K.

155 GAMES BOARD.
Germany, mid XVIIth Century.

Square, on wood carcase framed in tortoiseshell with ivory mouldings and inlaid lines; in the centre of each side a plaque of reddish transparent amber, formed of alternately octagonal and hexagonal panels, through which can be seen below an oval ivory plaque carved with a scene and surrounded by painted gilt scrollwork; the four minute scenes depict a mounted man (St. George?) rescuing a princess from a dragon.

Dimensions: 34.8 × 34.8 cm

The front of the games-board is composed of two rows of triangles converging on the centre, composed of transparent tortoiseshell applied over minute panels of grotesques painted in red, green and gold, alternating with panels of opaque amber of varying shade. The two rows of triangles are divided by a central band of five panels, alternately square and rectangular of transparent amber set over minute circular or rectangular scenes executed in a technique analogous to that of the frame. The panels are separated by ivory lines and by painted decorative motifs that can be seen through the tortoiseshell. On the four inner borders of the frame runs a Latin inscription with five words on each side. Each word is painted in gilt capital letters covered with a transparent layer of dark amber and is separated from the rest by minute rectangular inlays of transparent and of opaque amber.

The outside of the games-board is decorated with three panels on each side, the central one of green tortoiseshell, framed by ivory borders. At each corner a metal mount.

The opposite face of the board, designed for the game of *filetto* has an ivory frame, inset with geometrical panels of red tortoiseshell and with an ebony moulding along the sides running towards the centre. The central area is marked out for the game of *filetto* in ivory engraved with exceptional delicacy and further decorated with foliations in black. The ground in this case is of green and red tortoiseshell.

This work is usually associated with North Germany, in particular the Baltic coast. Besides games-boards, house-altars, caskets and knife handles were produced in the same workshops: most appear to date from the first half of the XVIIth century. A similar games-board is in the Milwaukee Museum of Art, U.S.A.; caskets, house-altars and knife handles decorated in this technique have survived in considerable number.

J. H.

156 ROCK CRYSTAL CROSS.
Italian, XIVth century, reconstructed in Germany, c. 1600.

The cross is built up of separate cylindrical and shaped elements of rock crystal fastened by silver rods which pass vertically and horizontally and are fixed at the ends by turned silver-gilt finials; between each element is a silver ring mount, the edges cut with trefoils, stepped ebonised wood base, the edges with gadrooned mouldings, the intervening spaces with applied silver mounts, probably from the workshop of Matthias Wallbaum of Angsbury.

Dimensions: H. 25 cm; W. 25 cm

This medieval rock crystal cross has been modernised in the late XVIth or XVIIth century by remounting and, probably, by replacement or addition of some rock crystal elements. Rock crystal was regarded as a particularly precious material in the Middle Ages, its clarity symbolising purity and such crosses were to be found in medieval treasuries. A similar Venetian rock crystal cross is in the Treasury of the Cathedral of Osnabrück. The remounting or modernisation of earlier reliquaries in the XVIth or XVIIth centuries was not unusual. Numerous examples were shown in the exhibition Les Trésors des Eglises de France, Paris, 1965[2].

1. W. Borchers, *Der Osnabrücker Domschatz,* Osnabrück, 1974, pl. 88.
2. See J. Taralon, *Treasures of the Churches of France,* London, 1966.

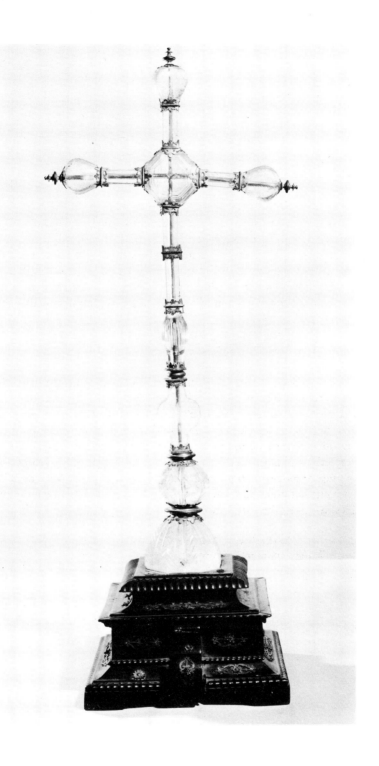

175